Farey Tales, The Lifeguard and Other Maths In...

for Higher-Level GCSE

Also available from Stanley Thornes (Publishers) Ltd:

Greer, A.   A Complete GCSE Mathematics: Basic Course
            A Complete GCSE Mathematics: General Course
            A Complete GCSE Mathematics: Higher Course

Smith, E.   Examples in Mathematics for GCSE
            Examples in Mathematics for GCSE – Higher Level
            Examples in Mathematics for GCSE – Foundation Level

Fairhurst, J.   Higher Level GCSE Mathematics

Bostock, L., Chandler, S., Shepherd, A. and Smith, E.   ST(P) Mathematics Resource Book

Farey Tales, The Lifeguard and Other Maths Investigations

for Higher-Level GCSE

Tony Croft

Department of Mathematical Sciences, Leicester Polytechnic

Derek Hart

Crewe & Alsager College of Higher Education

Stanley Thornes (Publishers) Ltd

First published in 1990 by:
Stanley Thornes (Publishers) Ltd
Old Station Drive
Leckhampton
CHELTENHAM GL53 0DN
England

British Library Cataloguing in Publication Data

Hart, Derek
Farey tales, the lifeguard and other maths investigations.
1. Mathematics
I. Title   II. Croft, Tony
510
ISBN 0–7487–0149–4

Typeset in 10/12 Novarese Book by Cotswold Typesetting Ltd, Cheltenham
Printed in Great Britain at The Bath Press, Avon

Contents

Acknowledgements

We would like to express appreciation to the following for their help in producing this book:

To Bob Davison, of Leicester Polytechnic, for collaborating with us to produce 'Safe driving', to Keith Walker, of Keele University for suggestions in 'Going round in circles', to Susan Oatway who performed much of the data collection in 'Literary fingerprinting', and to Keith Atkin for providing the photograph for 'Water spouts'.

Thanks must go to the B.Ed. Students at Crewe and Alsager College and to the teachers who have helped us try out these investigations. Procter and Gamble Ltd provided the information for 'Wash day', and the Kellogg Company of Great Britain provided packet sides for 'The breakfast-time matrix'. The information in 'Safe driving' is reproduced with permission from the Department of Transport.

Introduction

The Cockcroft Report, *Mathematics Counts*, (1982), emphasised the need for problem solving and investigational approaches to be incorporated into the secondary mathematics curriculum. Furthermore, the National Curriculum for mathematics requires, amongst other things, that pupils will be tested on their ability to carry out practical and investigational pieces of work, as well as discuss mathematical ideas. From 1991 all pupils sitting GCSE mathematics will be assessed on their course-work, the nature of which must be different from that of the examination. Thus the problem-solving/investigational approach has become central to all current mathematical educational thinking. All this, of course, has tremendous implications for the mathematics teacher. Many successful teachers now feel daunted by the prospect of the new approach; many non-specialist teachers who find themselves having to teach GCSE mathematics feel particularly intimidated by concepts of 'exploration', and the possibility of a problem not having a single correct answer (or maybe even no answer at all). Some of these apprehensions should be relieved by following the guidelines which follow and making use of the material in this book. Primarily, it is necessary to be flexible, to tolerate unusual and unanticipated approaches, and to move away from the idea that problems have a single correct method of solution. For the problems described in the following chapters, the emphasis must be on the quality of the processes undertaken rather than the answers achieved. To get the best out of any of the investigations, we suggest that the teacher tries out each one first to see the problem from the inside and to spot potential pitfalls and possible fruitful avenues. We have found it useful to pursue some sections individually and then discuss or compare results, and to tackle others collectively right from the start. It will undoubtedly be beneficial if time can be arranged to try out some investigations with teacher colleagues before using them in the classroom.

Before any investigational work is attempted it is necessary to introduce pupils to the various stages involved:

- an initial stage when the problem can be talked about, placed in context, etc., a strategy developed, and any necessary data or information gathered.
- a stage when ideas can be tried out, mathematical experiments and calculations performed, and results recorded.
- a stage when results can be analysed and patterns investigated. Conjectures can be formulated and tested.
- a stage when a final summary or report is prepared either verbally or in written form. Extensions to the problems undertaken can be identified.

These stages are intended to be general and are neither mutually exclusive nor exhaustive. A more detailed introduction is necessary for each individual investigation and this is described below.

Introductory sessions for individual investigations – general guidelines

If a session, or series of sessions, of investigational and problem-solving work is to be as beneficial as possible, a short introductory period is essential in which the teacher can explain to the pupils the broad area of investigation. They will then have a clear idea of the nature of the problem. Care is needed that this explanation doesn't turn into a prescriptive set of instructions, thereby invalidating the aims of the exercise. The following points can be used as a general checklist although particular investigations may require special introductory work and all the points listed may not be relevant to all the investigations.

1 Pupils should be made aware of the amount of time available in each session and of the number of sessions allocated to the investigation. However, this may not be possible in the more open-ended type of problem.

2 Pupils should be told what is expected of them e.g. regular discussions with the teacher relating their findings, oral report, written report, etc.

3 Is the investigation to be carried out individually or by groups of pupils? If a group is involved should a 'secretary' be appointed to keep written details of progress?

4 Any worksheets or datasheets, etc., should then be distributed.

5 It may be necessary to explain or revise mathematical pre-requisites although these ought to be framed generally so as not to prescribe one particular technique.

6 Some general tips and guidelines on strategy can be given. For example, pupils should be encouraged to:
(a) keep things as simple as possible, especially at the start.
(b) draw helpful diagrams.
(c) keep brief notes on their discoveries and thoughts or ideas which occur to them.
(d) try out or talk about ideas.
(e) later, consider and invent extensions or variations of the problem.

7 Pupils should not be afraid to ask for further assistance if necessary and know that this is available. They should be encouraged to inform the teacher of any discoveries of interest.

Assessment of investigations carried out by the more able pupils

The National Curriculum requires that pupils undertake extended pieces of work in which a range of activities can be carried out. Thus the assessment of such work is not simply a matter of giving a mark for a correct answer or method but should take into account a variety of other factors. The following points can be used to formulate a marking scheme although not all the points mentioned will be relevant to all investigations. Nevertheless, the more able pupils ought to be demonstrating evidence of their abilities in the areas listed. Examination boards have their own schemes of assessment so we have not included any attempt at marking schemes. The important points for consideration can be regarded as falling into four categories – understanding, planning, actually carrying out the necessary work, and summarising and communicating the findings. A photocopiable checklist is included on pp. 97–8.

Understanding
1 Is the pupil able to produce a clear statement of the problem either verbally or in written form, identifying its key features?

2 Is there evidence of a clear understanding?

Planning
3 Is the pupil able to formulate appropriate questions to be asked?

4 Can the pupil indicate where any necessary information or data can be obtained?

5 Is there evidence of a strategy developing?

6 Can the pupil recognise how a situation can be interpreted mathematically?

7 Can an appropriate method for tackling the problem be identified?

Carrying out the investigation
8 Can the pupil gather necessary information either from worksheets/datasheets, books, or from other sources available, for example, in the library?

9 Does the pupil understand the data that has been given or found?

10 Can the pupil extract from an amount of information or data, its relevant parts?

11 Can the pupil make relevant calculations, demonstrate mathematical knowledge and answer technical questions?

12 Is the pupil able to draw conclusions, identify patterns, etc?

13 Can areas of further investigation be identified?

14 Can the pupil suggest modifications to the problem and invent new problems?

15 Is there the suggestion of comparison of a variety of techniques for tackling a problem?

16 Can the pupil work in a logical and organised way either

(a) individually or **(b)** cooperatively?

17 Is the pupil aware of any assumptions which have been made?

Summarising and communicating
18 Can the pupil write up a clear report of the investigation – identifying any findings and making wide and effective use of mathematical language?

19 Can the pupil identify what has been learnt?

20 Is the pupil aware of the dependence of conclusions on assumptions already made?

21 Can any findings be communicated orally to
(a) the teacher and **(b)** other pupils?

22 Can the pupil identify any shortcomings? Is the validity of any models used questioned?

Finally, the investigational approach can be a very worthwhile, interesting and rewarding activity both for the teacher and pupil. The whole concept of a problem-solving approach should be tremendously dynamic and the investigations described in this book whilst they can be regarded as complete in themselves, really ought to be used as starting points. It is only by carrying out investigations that ideas for others will spring to mind and we encourage teachers to absorb themselves in the topic. If the teacher can convey an enthusiasm to the pupils the learning process will become all the easier. We hope that the following chapters will convince you of this.

Reading between the lines

The tables below appeared in a guidebook of car prices and show what you might expect to pay for a second-hand car depending on its year of registration and its condition. The prices in the guidebook allow for such factors as ageing, fair wear and tear, maintenance, etc.

You will notice from the tables that various entries are missing owing to a printer's error. Investigate various ways in which the missing data can be estimated and the tables completed.

YEAR	A1	GOOD	FAIR

CITROEN

2-CV 6 4d Saloon (Club from Jan '82) IG 1

YEAR	A1	GOOD	FAIR
1975	385	325	200
1976	525	450	295
1977	685	580	400
1978		750	
1979	1050	900	
1980	1250	1100	750
1981	1525		925
1982	1850	1635	1135
1983	2225	1975	1400

ROLLS-ROYCE

Corniche 2d DH Coupe (Silver Shadow Park Ward pre Oct '71) IG 7/8

YEAR	A1	GOOD	FAIR
1973	13575	12225	8450
1974	15675	14075	11000
1975	18100	15375	12250
1976	21300	19100	14550
1977		22425	16950
1978	28800	25825	19775
1979	33700	30050	23300
1980	39000	34950	27400
1981	45900		32700
1982	53225	47900	38300
1983	60500	54500	

© Tony Croft and Derek Hart,
Farey Tales, The Lifeguard and Other Maths Investigations for Higher-Level GCSE,
Stanley Thornes, 1990

Reading between the lines: Teaching notes

This investigation is concerned with finding missing values in a table of data. A variety of approaches are possible. We suggest that pupils are given the worksheet and graph paper and then left to devise appropriate ways of completing the table. Once a method has been found they should be encouraged to discover other solutions and try to decide which method, if any, is best and why.

Various approaches

(a) Graphical

Certainly, it is helpful to have the data displayed graphically so that overall trends can be identified and a graph such as that in Figure 1 should lead to other ways of estimating the missing values. Perhaps, if the horizontal axis were relabelled 'back-to-front' the depreciation would be more apparent.

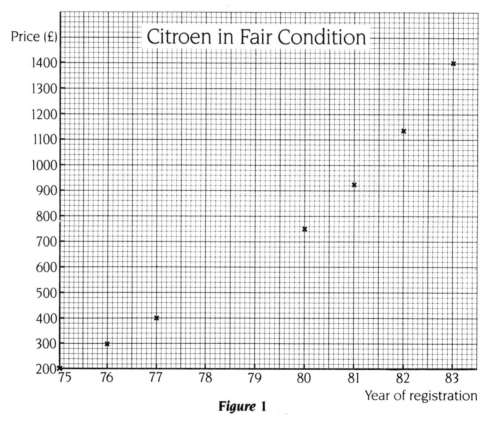

Figure 1

(b) Averaging

When only one data item is missing and this point occurs half-way between two known values, the mean will provide an estimate of the missing value.

(c) Linear interpolation

Approach (b) is a particular case of linear interpolation. Some pupils may suggest the calculation of the equation of the straight line joining two known points. From this equation an estimate of the missing value is easily obtained.

(d) Similar triangles

Similar triangles can be used.

Approaches (c) and (d) are particularly useful when the missing data is not half-way between two known points.

(e) Line of best fit

When the data possesses some linearity a line of best fit could be drawn by eye, passing through the mean of the *x* and *y* values.

Warning: To complete the table some extrapolation is also necessary. This may be an appropriate time to mention to pupils some of the dangers of extrapolating data too far into the past or the future!

Some solutions

(a) Citroen in fair condition

To find the missing value for 1978.

We have the similar triangles shown:

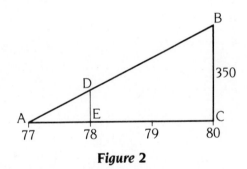

Figure 2

$\triangle$ADE is similar to $\triangle$ABC (corresponding angles the same).

$$\frac{DE}{BC} = \frac{AE}{AC}$$

$$\frac{DE}{350} = \frac{1}{3}$$

so that $\qquad$ DE $= 116.67$

This gives a price of £516.67 for a 1978 Citroen in fair condition.

(b) Citroen in A1 condition

To find the missing value for 1978.

Taking the mean value of the two prices on either side gives a price of £867.50 for a 1978 model.

3

(c) Rolls Royce Silver Shadow in fair condition

To find the missing value for 1983.

The equation of the straight line joining (81, 32 700) and (82, 38 300), is

$$y = 5600x - 420\ 900$$

When $x = 83$, $y = 43\ 900$. This estimate compares well with the missing value which was, in fact, £43 500.

Extensions and extended projects

Obtain a copy of a recent used-car price guide, and ask the pupils to assume that they have a certain amount of money to spend on a nearly-new car. Ask them to investigate the rates at which different makes of car appear to depreciate, and so come up with a list of cars which are both affordable and will realise the best return when the time comes to trade them in.

Ms Whizz's charity run – an introduction to arithmetic progressions

Last week I decided to take up jogging to raise money for a school minibus. A local firm offered to sponsor me an amount of £1 for each mile I managed to jog. The trouble is that all these years in front of a blackboard have made me very unfit so I decided to start off quite modestly.

Last Monday I managed to jog one mile. As the days went by I found myself getting much fitter and the running getting much easier. Each day I could run half a mile more than the previous day. What I'd like you to do in this investigation is find some formulae to tell me:

(a) How far will I be able to run *next* Monday (a week after I started)?

(b) How far will I be able to run any number of days after I started?

(c) On which day will I first manage to run 8 miles?

(d) How much money will I have raised in total after any given number of days?

It's formulae I'm after, so don't simply start working it all out day by day. To help you solve these problems, investigate the following first.

Here is a sequence of numbers: 1, 2, 3, 4, 5.

What is the rule?

Here is another sequence: − 3, − 1, 1, 3, 5, 7.

What is the rule now?

You will have probably noticed that in both cases a **fixed** amount is added on each time. Sequences like these are called **arithmetic progressions**, and the amount you have added on is called the **common difference**.

© Tony Croft and Derek Hart,
*Farey Tales, The Lifeguard and Other
Maths Investigations for Higher-Level GCSE,*
Stanley Thornes, 1990

Write down two more arithmetic progressions each containing five terms, each starting with 1, with common differences of 3 and 5 respectively. Find a formula which tells you the last term in each case.

Suppose you have more than 5 terms. Can you find a formula telling you the nth term where n could be any positive whole number?

The sum, which we'll call S, of all the terms of the first progression we wrote down above is

$$1 + 2 + 3 + 4 + 5 = 15.$$

Suppose there had been a lot more terms. Can you find a quick way of adding them all up to find S?

Hint: S can be written

$$S = 1 + 2 + 3 + 4 + 5$$

and also as $\qquad S = 5 + 4 + 3 + 2 + 1$

If we add these two ways of writing S together we get

$$2S = 6 + 6 + 6 + 6 + 6$$

There are 5 terms, so

$$2S = 5 \times 6 = 30$$

and so $\qquad S = 15.$

Go through the same process with other arithmetic progressions to find a way of adding up all the terms easily.

Finally, can you find a general formula which will add up the terms of any arithmetic progression if you are given the starting value, a, say, and the number of terms, n?

Use your formula to find the sum of all the even numbers from 0 to 1000.

Use it to find the sum of all the multiples of 5 from 25 to 2500.

With all this experience you should now be able to help me solve my jogging problems.

Ms Whizz's charity run: Teaching notes

The arithmetic progressions with first term 1 and common differences 3 and 5 are

$$1, 4, 7, 10, 13$$

and

$$1, 6, 11, 16, 21$$

respectively.

The last term = the first term plus 4 common differences

i.e.

$$1 + 4(3) = 13$$

and

$$1 + 4(5) = 21$$

respectively.

Generally, the nth term = first term plus $(n-1)$ common differences.

Summing the progression $1, 4, 7, 10, 13$ in two ways we get

$$\begin{aligned} S &= 1 + 4 + 7 + 10 + 13 \\ S &= 13 + 10 + 7 + 4 + 1 \\ \hline 2S &= 14 + 14 + 14 + 14 + 14 \\ &= 5(14) = 70 \end{aligned}$$

and $+$

so that $S = 35$.

Twice the sum is always n times (the first plus last terms) so that generally,

$$S = \frac{n}{2}(\text{first term} + \text{last term})$$

But the nth term is $a + (n-1)d$, where d is the common difference, so

$$S = \frac{n}{2}\{a + [a + (n-1)d]\}$$

$$= \frac{n}{2}[2a + (n-1)d]$$

The sum of the even numbers from 0 to 1000 is 250 500.

The sum of all the multiples of 5 from 25 to 2500 is 626 200.

Ms Whizz's charity run

(a) The following Monday is the 8th day.
Number of miles $= 1 + 7(\text{common difference}) = 4\frac{1}{2}$ miles.

(b) Generally, the number of miles $= 1 + \frac{1}{2}(\text{number of days} - 1)$.

(c) We require the day on which the term in the progression is 8.

$$8 = 1 + \tfrac{1}{2}(\text{number of days} - 1)$$

so that the number of days is 15.
On the 15th day Ms Whizz first manages to run 8 miles.

7

(d) After m days the sum of money raised = sum of miles run

$$= \frac{m}{2}\{1 + [1 + \tfrac{1}{2}(m-1)]\}$$

$$= \frac{m}{4}(3 + m)$$

Can of worms

When you've been taking your dog for a walk along the canal bank have you noticed the men sitting huddled in their coats? Sometimes they have large umbrellas, they nearly all smoke, and most wear flat caps; they all look bored. These men are the spiritual descendants of Izaak Walton. They are all partakers in Britain's most popular sport – fishing. My Uncle George noticed them. He also noticed that among empty beer or coke cans and the half eaten pork pie is the *can*! It is always there. A largish cylindrical can full of sawdust and wriggling grubs. Uncle George is a man of business acumen and wondered where all these millions of fishermen got these cans. Apparently, fishermen go to the cash and carry shops, buy a hotel/catering size of Oxford Rough Cut Marmalade, rush home, open the can and throw away the contents. Billy-ho! There it is!

Uncle George decided to enter the Metal Box world. He found that these cans must have a capacity of 8 litres. He set about making the cans. He reckoned he could sell them a lot cheaper than at the cash and carry, full of marmalade. The trouble is he is a mean old thing and wanted to use the least amount of sheet metal to make the cost as little as possible. Although the can was traditionally cylindrical he reckoned the shape didn't matter. He decided to design not only cylindrical ones, but also one with a rectangular base with either vertical or sloping sides, and one with a circular base which could either be cylindrical or conical. Of course, it had to be stable, so the base couldn't be too small. On the other hand, the base had to be made of a double thickness of metal for strength. A single thickness of metal was needed for the lid. In all cases the volume had to be 8 litres and he wanted to keep the cost to a minimum. The cost of a single thickness of sheet metal is £1.50 per square metre, so the cost for the base is £3 per square metre.

Investigate possible designs for the fisherman's can. Find the cost of the metal required to make cans you think satisfy all the above criteria.

© Tony Croft and Derek Hart,
*Farey Tales, The Lifeguard and Other
Maths Investigations for Higher-Level GCSE,*
Stanley Thornes, 1990

Can of worms: Teaching notes

It is important at the outset for pupils to be clear about the units in which they wish to work. Suppose we decide to work in metres.

$$8 \text{ litres} = 0.008 \text{ m}^3$$

The most straightforward case to deal with is probably that of a cubic can. If the can has sides x (Figure 1), then in order to have the correct capacity we require

$$x^3 = 0.008 \text{ m}^3$$

so that $\qquad\qquad x = 0.2 \text{ m}$

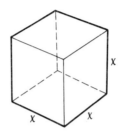

Figure 1

The cost of materials to make such a can would be

$$£1.5(5x^2) \quad \text{for the sides and top}$$

and $\qquad\qquad £3(x^2) \quad$ for the double-thickness base,

giving, in this case, a cost of 42p per can.

However, this is by no means the optimum design.

Another relatively straightforward case to deal with is that of a cylindrical can with dimensions as shown in Figure 2.

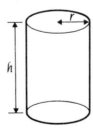

Figure 2

In this case we have $\pi r^2 h = 0.008$. [1]

Pupils may wish to calculate the cost of materials for a variety of values of r, with h being determined from [1].

An improved technique would be to write down an expression for the cost.

$$\text{Cost of top} = 1.5\pi r^2$$

$$\text{Cost of cylindrical sides} = 1.5(2\pi rh)$$

$$\text{Cost of base} = 3\pi r^2$$

So the total cost, C, in pounds is

$$C = 3\pi rh + 4.5\pi r^2$$

Eliminating h using [1] we have

$$C = \frac{0.024}{r} + 4.5\pi r^2$$

From a table of values, a graph of C against r can be drawn (Figure 3), and the minimum cost and optimum radius identified, at about 38p and 9.5 cm respectively.

r(m)	0.01	0.02	0.03	0.04	0.05	0.06	0.07	0.08
C(£)	2.401	1.206	0.813	0.623	0.515	0.451	0.412	0.390

r(m)	0.09	0.10	0.11	0.12	0.13	0.14	0.15
C(£)	0.381	0.381	0.389	0.404	0.424	0.449	0.478

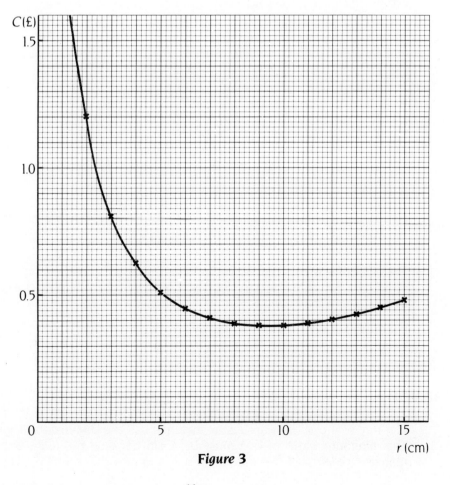

Figure 3

Can the cost be reduced further by using a conical shape? Certainly a reduction in the size of the base and a corresponding increase in the size of the lid should help since the base costs twice as much per unit area as the lid. There is no unique answer to this problem since, in theory, the base can be made smaller and smaller, but on the other hand we want the can to stand freely. Formulae are needed to give the volume and surface area of the frustrum of a cone. We suggest that the pupils are not given this information until they have identified exactly what is required.

Information

The volume of a (right circular) cone $= \frac{1}{3}\pi r^2 h$

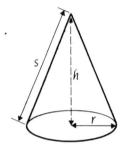

Figure 4

and its curved surface area $= \pi r s$

with $\qquad s = \sqrt{h^2 + r^2}$

The volume of a frustrum of a cone $= \frac{1}{3}\pi h(r_1^2 + r_1 r_2 + r_2^2)$

and its curved surface area is $\quad \pi s(r_1 + r_2)$

with $\qquad s = \sqrt{h^2 + (r_1 - r_2)^2}.$

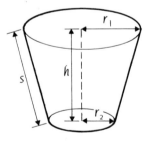

Figure 5

The algebra is more complicated now but in order to proceed why not fix the base radius at a 'sensible' size (smaller than 0.095 m), 0.08 m, say, and the radius of the top at, say, 0.11 m. The previous formulae then give $h = 0.280$ m and $s = 0.282$ m.

Finally, the cost would be 37p per can.

Extension

The tray of a box of Swan Vestas matches has the dimensions shown in Figure 6. The minimum width of box must be 4 cm because the manufacturers want the matches (of length 3.75 cm) to lie in this, and only this, direction. The volume of the

12

box must be 30 cm³ in order to hold 90 matches. It will be helpful if such a matchbox is available. Although this design is traditional and well-liked, it may not be the most economical. Is it possible to reduce the length of the box, and increase its height, to reduce the amount of card needed?

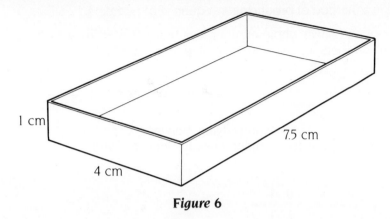

Figure 6

As a first attempt at the solution of the problem a simple net of the tray can be drawn.

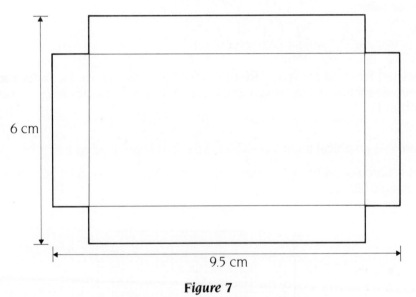

Figure 7

In reality, the net of the tray, and the net of the surrounding tube of card is more complicated, as various extra pieces are included in order to make a securely-glued structure, thus making some of the sides 'double-thickness' as in the previous investigation. The study of this structure, and investigation of ways of optimising the design provide the framework for a detailed extended piece of work.

Farey sequences 1

Here is a method of producing a sequence of numbers.

Think of a positive whole number less than 10. Starting with 0, write down all the whole numbers up to and including that number. For example, suppose you thought of 2, then write down 0, 1, 2.

Now, write down all the different proper fractions that can be formed from these numbers.

Proper fractions are fractions lying between 0 and 1, so you wouldn't include numbers like $\frac{2}{1}$ but, for completeness, we include $\frac{0}{1}$ and $\frac{1}{1}$.

In our case:

$$\frac{0}{1}, \frac{1}{1}, \frac{1}{2}.$$

Next, arrange these fractions in order of size starting with $\frac{0}{1}$ and ending with $\frac{1}{1}$.

In our case:

$$\frac{0}{1}, \frac{1}{2}, \frac{1}{1}.$$

This sequence, which is an ordered list of fractions, is called a **Farey sequence**. The Farey sequence above which uses only the whole numbers 0, 1 and 2 is often written F_2.

Here is a graphical technique which we could have used to find F_2.

On squared or graph paper mark the points $(0, 0)$, $(2, 0)$, and $(2, 2)$. Join them to make a triangle (Figure 1).

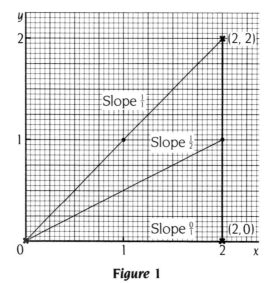

Figure 1

© Tony Croft and Derek Hart,
*Farey Tales, The Lifeguard and Other
Maths Investigations for Higher-Level GCSE,*
Stanley Thornes, 1990

Draw straight lines from the origin to the grid points inside or on the sides of the triangle. Calculate the slopes of all the different lines. The horizontal line has a slope of $\frac{0}{1}$; going up in order of steepness we get

$$\frac{0}{1}, \frac{1}{2}, \frac{1}{1}.$$

These three fractions form the Farey sequence F_2.

Can you generalise this method to find $F_1, F_3, F_4, \ldots F_7$?

Investigation: Properties of Farey sequences

1   Investigate the relationship between two consecutive terms of a sequence?

(Hint: Suppose $\frac{a}{b}$ and $\frac{c}{d}$ are consecutive terms.

Find a relationship between $a, b, c,$ and d.)

2 $\frac{1}{3}$ and $\frac{1}{2}$ are non-consecutive terms of F_6.

Note that

$$\frac{1+1}{3+2} = \frac{2}{5}$$

is also a term of F_6 and lies between them. Is the same true of $\frac{1}{4}$ and $\frac{3}{5}$ in F_6? Explain!

Suppose that $\frac{a}{b}$ and $\frac{c}{d}$ are non-consecutive terms of a Farey sequence.

Can you discover under what circumstances

$$\frac{a+c}{b+d}$$

is also in the sequence?

3   Is it true that the terms of a Farey sequence are contained in the next highest Farey sequence? For example, is it true that F_3 is contained in F_4? Use a diagram to explain your answer.

Farey sequences 1: Teaching notes

John Farey was a Scot who lived in the Napoleonic era. He wrote on many topics including geology, music, decimal currency, carriage wheels, comets and Farey sequences.

The grid method of determining a Farey sequence, F_n, can be used for any n. Draw a triangle by joining points $(0, 0)$, $(n, 0)$ and (n, n).

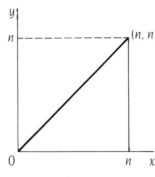

Figure 2

If lines are drawn from the origin to all grid points contained by the triangle, the gradients of these lines in ascending order form the Farey sequence.

Investigation: Properties of Farey sequences

1 If $\dfrac{a}{b}$ and $\dfrac{c}{d}$ are consecutive terms in a Farey sequence, then
$$ad - bc = -1$$

2 The numerator of any fraction in a Farey sequence is obtained by adding the numerators of the terms on either side in the sequence. A similar rule applies for the denominators.

3 F_n is contained in F_{n+1} for all n.

This can be easily seen from a diagram, since the triangle of grid points which gives F_n is totally contained within the triangle which gives F_{n+1}.

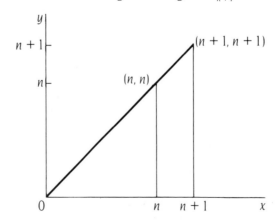

Figure 3

Farey sequences 2

How many and how much?

1 If N is the number of terms in the Farey sequence F_n, complete the table below for values of n from 1 to 4.

n	Number of terms in F_n N
1	
2	
3	
4	

Can you deduce a rule for finding N given n?
Does your rule fit F_5 and F_6?
Is there a rule for F_5 and F_6?
What about F_7 and F_8?

2 There is a relationship between the number of terms in a Farey sequence and what are called the Euler Numbers, $E(n)$. First you will need to learn about these.
Suppose you wanted to find the Euler Number $E(4)$.
Write down the factors of 4.
Write down all the positive integers less than 4, i.e. 1, 2, 3.
Look at the numbers you have just written down and cross out all those that share a factor with 4, excluding 1. Since 2 is a factor of 2, and it is also a factor of 4, we cross it out. Since 1 and 3 share no factors with 4 we don't cross these out. We are left with just *two* numbers 1 and 3. The number of numbers we are left with is the required Euler number, in this case $E(4) = 2$.
Show that $E(6) = 2$.

Complete the following table:

n	Number of terms in F_n N	$E(n)$
1	2	1
2		
3		
4		2
5		
6		2
7		
8		

Can you now deduce a relationship between N and $E(n)$? Check your answers with F_9 and F_{10}.

© Tony Croft and Derek Hart,
*Farey Tales, The Lifeguard and Other
Maths Investigations for Higher-Level GCSE,*
Stanley Thornes, 1990

3 The Farey sequence F_4 is

$$\frac{0}{1}, \frac{1}{4}, \frac{1}{3}, \frac{1}{2}, \frac{2}{3}, \frac{3}{4}, \frac{1}{1}.$$

Notice that $\frac{1}{2}$ is the middle term. Is this true for other Farey sequences? Notice also that the terms equidistant from $\frac{1}{2}$ add up to 1.

e.g.
$$\frac{1}{4} + \frac{3}{4} = 1$$

Does this apply to other Farey sequences?
Can you use this fact to find the sum of the terms of a Farey sequence?
Can you deduce a formula connecting the sum of the terms of F_n with $E(n)$?
Do you notice anything special about $E(n)$ when n is a prime number?

© Tony Croft and Derek Hart,
*Farey Tales, The Lifeguard and Other
Maths Investigations for Higher-Level GCSE,*
Stanley Thornes, 1990

Farey sequences 2: Teaching notes

1

n	No of terms in F_n N
1	2
2	3
3	5
4	7
5	11
6	13
7	19
8	23
9	29
10	33

For $n = 2, 3, 4$, pupils may suggest the rule $N = 2n - 1$, but this rule breaks down for $n \geqq 5$.

For $n = 5, 6$, pupils may suggest $N = 2n + 1$, but again the rule fails for $n > 6$.

2

n	No of terms in F_n N	$E(n)$
1	2	1
2	3	1
3	5	2
4	7	2
5	11	4
6	13	2
7	19	6
8	23	4
9	29	6
10	33	4

The number of terms in F_n, $N = E(2) + E(3) + \ldots + E(n) + 2$.

3 Note from the above table that for $n > 1$, N is always odd. The middle term of a Farey sequence is always $\frac{1}{2}$ and fractions equidistant from $\frac{1}{2}$ add up to 1.

Therefore, the sum of the terms $= N/2$.

Consequently this sum also equals

$$\frac{E(2) + E(3) + \ldots + E(n) + 2}{2}$$

When n is prime, $E(n) = n - 1$.

Safe driving

Investigation 1

The Highway Code gives much advice to drivers and pedestrians about how to use the road safely. This investigation concerns the advice and information given regarding stopping distances for cars, and the gaps which should be maintained between the vehicles.

On the back page of the Highway Code is a chart giving information about stopping distances of cars travelling at various speeds. The distances given are *shortest* stopping distances for an average family car. They assume the car has efficient brakes, the road surface is ideal (i.e. not wet or icy) and the car tyres are in good condition.

Shortest stopping distances

At 30 mph

Thinking distance	Braking distance	Overall stopping distance
9 m	**14 m**	**23 m**
30 ft	**45 ft**	**75 ft**

At 50 mph

Thinking distance	Braking distance	Overall stopping distance
15 m	**38 m**	**53 m**
50 ft	**125 ft**	**175 ft**

At 70 mph

Thinking distance	Braking distance	Overall stopping distance
21 m	**75 m**	**96 m**
70 ft	**245 ft**	**315 ft**

Imagine a driver in his car. He decides to brake. Between deciding to brake and pressing his foot on the brake pedal a short time will elapse – the thinking time. During this thinking period the car will travel a certain distance known as the 'thinking distance'. Once the brake is applied the car begins to decelerate and finally stops. The distance it travels while the brake is applied is the 'braking distance'. The overall stopping distance is the sum of the thinking distance and the braking distance.

Overall stopping distance = Thinking distance + Braking distance

In order to analyse the equations connecting speed and distance a notation is introduced.

v = speed of car in mph
T_d = thinking distance in feet
B_d = braking distance in feet

s = overall stopping distance in feet
t = time in seconds

© Tony Croft and Derek Hart,
*Farey Tales, The Lifeguard and Other
Maths Investigations for Higher-Level GCSE,*
Stanley Thornes, 1990

1 Plot a graph of T_d against v. From your graph determine the thinking distance when the speed is 43 mph.

2 Determine an equation connecting T_d and v.

3 Use the information in the chart to draw a graph of B_d against v.
From your graph determine the braking distance when the speed is 52 mph.
If the braking distance is 200 feet, what is the speed of the car?

4 The equation connecting B_d and v is thought to be a quadratic,

$$B_d = av^2 + bv + c$$

where a, b and c are constants.

What is the braking distance when the car is stationary?
What does this tell us about the value of c?

Use the pairs of values $B_d = 45$ when $v = 30$, and $B_d = 125$ when $v = 50$ to find the values of a and b. Write down the quadratic equation connecting B_d and v.

Calculate the braking distance when the speed is 70 mph using the quadratic equation. Compare it with the value given in the Highway Code when v is 70.

5 Write down an equation connecting the overall stopping distance, s, to the speed, v.
Calculate s when $v = 30, 50, 70$ and compare with the values given in the Highway Code.
What is the overall stopping distance for a car travelling at 64 mph?

6 To avoid an accident happening in a 40 mph zone a driver brakes sharply. The length of the skid mark is 75 feet. How fast do you think the car was travelling? Was the driver speeding? Estimate the overall stopping distance of the car.

Safe driving: Teaching notes

Investigation 1

1

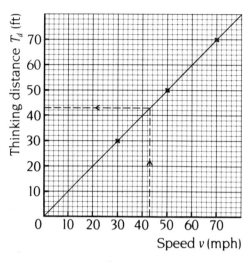

Figure 1

Note, if the speed is zero, there will be no thinking distance so the graph will pass through the origin. With the data given, it is reasonable to assume the relationship is linear.

When $v = 43$ mph, $T_d = 43$ ft.

2 $T_d = v$

3 It is clear that the three given points do not lie on a straight line. A further point can be introduced if it is realised that when the speed is zero, the braking distance must be zero. Pupils can either draw straight line segments to estimate missing values, or sketch the curve through the three or four points (see Chapter 1).

From Figure 2 (opposite), when $v = 52$ mph, $B_d = 135$ ft.

When $B_d = 200$ ft, $v = 63.25$ mph.

4 $c = 0$

Given $B_d = 45$ when $v = 30$, and $B_d = 125$ when $v = 50$ we have the simultaneous equations

$$45 = a(30)^2 + 30b$$

$$125 = a(50)^2 + 50b$$

with solution $a = 0.05, \quad b = 0$

$$\therefore B_d = 0.05\, v^2, \text{ or } B_d = \frac{v^2}{20}$$

When $v = 70$ mph, $B_d = 245$ ft, the same as the Highway Code.

22

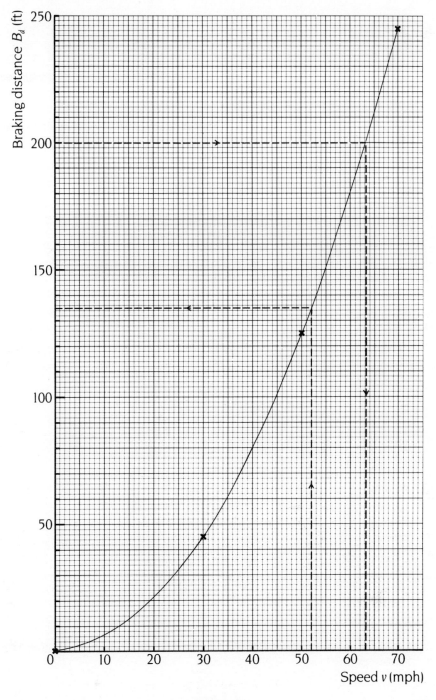

Figure 2

5

$$s = \frac{v^2}{20} + v$$

When $v = 64$ mph, $s = 268.8$ ft.

6

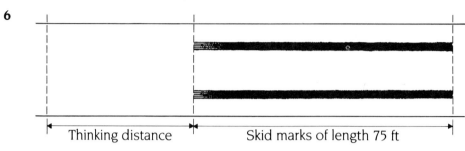

Thinking distance | Skid marks of length 75 ft

Figure 3

Assume that the length of the skid mark is the braking distance.

If $B_d = 75$ ft, then v must have been 38.7 mph so the driver was probably not speeding.
$T_d = 38.7$ ft so the overall stopping distance was 113.7 ft.

Safe driving

Investigation 2

Section 51 of the Highway Code states the following:

> ... The safe rule is never to get closer (to the vehicle in front) than the overall stopping distance ... But on the open road, in good conditions, a gap of one metre for each mph of your speed or a two-second time gap may be enough ...

There appear to be *three* recommendations in Section 51.
The distance or gap between vehicles should be:

(A) at least the overall stopping distance
(B) one metre for each mph of speed
(C) 2 seconds.

1 This part of the problem refers to recommendation B. Taking 1 metre to equal 3.3 feet complete the table.

Speed (mph)	Gap (metres)	Gap (feet)
20	20	66
30	30	
40		
50		
60		
70		

Plot a graph of gap in feet against speed in mph.

2 This part of the question refers to recommendation C. A gap of 2 seconds is converted into an equivalent distance gap. Given 10 mph = 14.67 feet/sec, complete the table.

Speed (mph)	Distance (feet) travelled in 1 second	Gap (feet)
20	29.34	58.68
30	44.01	
40		
50		
60		
70		

Plot a graph of gap in feet against speed.

© Tony Croft and Derek Hart,
*Farey Tales, The Lifeguard and Other
Maths Investigations for Higher-Level GCSE,*
Stanley Thornes, 1990

3 The graphs of the three recommendations are now plotted on the same axes so that the recommendations can be compared.

Plot the 3 'gap graphs' using the same axes.

Graph 1: gap = overall stopping distance
Graph 2: gap = 1 metre for each mph
Graph 3: gap is 2 seconds.

4 Which is the safest recommendation? Is it the same recommendation for all speeds? Why are recommended gaps given in terms of both time and distance?

Safe driving: Teaching notes

Investigation 2

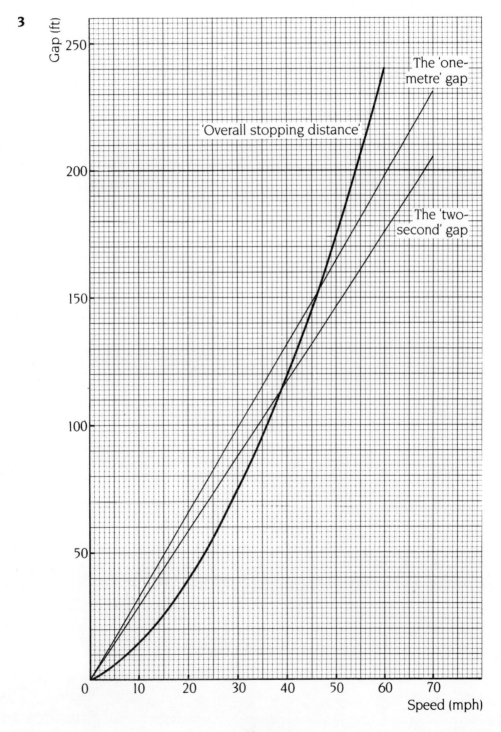

3

Figure 4

4 The 'safest' recommendation depends upon the speed. At high speeds, the 'overall stopping distance' will be safer than either of the other two gaps whereas, at low speeds, the 'one-metre' gap is the safest. At all speeds the 'one-metre' gap is safer than the 'two-second' gap. At about 45 mph the 'overall stopping distance' and 'one-metre' rule are equally safe.

Iteration I

Teaching notes

Introduction

The sequence of numbers $x_1, x_2, \ldots, x_n$, may or may not converge. If it does, then the terms will progressively get closer to a number called the **limit** of the sequence. For example, the sequence

$$1, 1\tfrac{1}{2}, 1\tfrac{3}{4}, 1\tfrac{7}{8}, \ldots$$

gets closer and closer to 2. On the other hand, the sequence

$$2, 4, 6, 8, 10, \ldots$$

does not converge and the terms get larger and larger.

Sometimes a sequence can be described by giving an algebraic expression for the general term.

The sequence $2, 4, 8, 16, \ldots$ is given by the rule: the nth term is 2^n.

that is $x_n = 2^n$

Sometimes a sequence is defined recursively, that is, the nth term depends upon the previous terms. One of the most well-known examples of this is the Fibonacci sequence

$$1, 1, 2, 3, 5, 8, 13, \ldots$$

where, apart from the first and second terms, each term is the sum of the two previous ones.

$$x_n = x_{n-1} + x_{n-2}$$

Investigation 1

Use the square-root button on a calculator to investigate the convergence or divergence of the sequence

$$x_{n+1} = \sqrt{x_n}$$

For example, set $x_0 = 5$ and then we obtain

$$x_1 = 2.2361$$

$$x_2 = 1.4953$$

$$\ldots$$

$$x_{24} = 1$$

$$x_{25} = 1$$

All that this calculation involves is the repeated pressing of the square root button on a calculator.

'1' is called the **fixed point** of the sequence. Ask pupils to investigate whether or not the sequence converges to 1 for any initial value x_0.

Investigation 2

This time the sequence under investigation is

$$x_{n+1} = \sqrt{ax_n}$$

where a is some positive number. Select a large value of a, say, $a = 1000$ and a starting value, $x_0 = 10$. Pupils should use their calculators to investigate convergence or divergence for a variety of values of x_0 and a. Ask them to complete a table such as:

Value of a	Value of limit
1000	1000
100	
50	
20	
5	
0.2	

Conclusion: the sequence $x_{n+1} = \sqrt{ax_n}$ converges to ...

Investigation 3

Ask pupils to consider the sequences generated by the following formula:

$$x_{n+1} = \sqrt{\sqrt{ax_n}}$$

with a again being a positive number.

For example, if $a = 20$ and $x_0 = 3$, the limit is 2.7144. Keeping a fixed, pupils can verify that the limit is always 2.7144 provided $x_0 > 0$. Again, a table can be produced:

Value of a	Value of limit
1000	
100	
50	
20	2.7144
10	
3	
0.2	

What is the relationship between a and the limit?

Investigation 4

The three previous investigations have been special cases of the sequence defined by

$$x_{n+1} = (ax_n)^{1/m}$$

In order to perform this investigation pupils should be familiar with the x^y or $x^{1/y}$ buttons on their scientific calculators. As an illustration, take the value of a to be 20 and $m = 3$.

With $x_0 = 20$, the sequence 20, 7.368, 5.282, ..., is obtained which converges to 4.472. What is the relation between this limit and 20?

Keeping $m = 3$, try different values of a. Does the same relationship exist between a and the limit?

Now try different values of m, greater than 1. What now is the relationship between a, m and the limit? Eventually a table such as the one below can be produced:

Value of m	Value of limit
2	a
3	$a^{1/2}$
4	
5	

Conclusion: the sequence $x_{n+1} = (ax_n)^{1/m}$ converges to ...

As long as the values of a and x_0 are positive the limit is $a^{1/m-1}$.

Finally, investigate generalisations to other sequences which use the square-root button in some way or other.

Iteration II

Teaching notes

Investigation 1

Many sequences defined recursively will converge for some starting values but will diverge for others.

Consider $x_{n+1} = x_n^2$

If $x_0 = 0.5$, then $x_1 = 0.25$, $x_2 = 0.0625$ and so on. The sequence approaches the limit 0. However, if $x_0 = 2$, then $x_1 = 4$, $x_2 = 16$ and the sequence diverges. Pupils can investigate which starting values will converge and which will diverge in the following cases:

$x_{n+1} = (x_n - 1)^2 + 1$

converges to 1 if $0 < x_0 < 2$,
converges to 2 if $x_0 = 2$ or 0,
diverges otherwise.

$x_{n+1} = (x_n - 1)^3 + 1$

converges to 2 if $x_0 = 2$,
converges to 0 if $x_0 = 0$,
converges to 1 if $0 < x_0 < 2$,
diverges otherwise.

$x_{n+1} = -(x_n^3)$

Strangely, if $x_0 = \pm 1$, the sequence oscillates between $+1$ and -1 indefinitely,
i.e. it neither converges nor diverges.

If $-1 < x_0 < 1$, it converges to zero.

If $x_0 > 1$ or $x_0 < -1$ it diverges.

Investigation 2

A common iterative scheme for finding the square root of a number K is

$$x_{n+1} = \frac{1}{2}\left(x_n + \frac{K}{x_n}\right)$$

Pupils can investigate this iteration for a variety of values of positive integers K.

Iteration III

Teaching notes

If we have to solve a quadratic equation there are several methods available to us. The left-hand side of the equation may factorise:

$$x^2 + x - 6 = 0$$

$$(x - 2)(x + 3) = 0$$

so that $\qquad x = 2 \text{ or } x = -3$

We can also complete the square.

$$x^2 + 12x + 4 = 0$$

$$(x + 6)^2 - 36 + 4 = 0$$

$$(x + 6)^2 = 32$$

and from this last equation we can find the required values of x.

Alternatively, we can use the well-known formula.

$$x^2 + x - 1 = 0$$

$$x = \frac{-1 \pm \sqrt{1 + 4}}{2}$$

$$= \frac{-1 \pm \sqrt{5}}{2}$$

$$= 0.618 \text{ or } -1.618$$

Iterative methods provide another way of tackling the solution of equations and they are not restricted to the solution of quadratic equations.

Suppose we want to solve

$$x^2 - 5x - 7 = 0$$

We can rearrange the equation as

$$x = \sqrt{7 + 5x}$$

We can choose a value of x and feed it into the right-hand side of the rearranged equation. Repeating the process with the new value of x gives rise to a sequence of values which may or may not converge to the root of the equation. In this case suppose we start with $x_0 = 6$.

Then $\qquad x_1 = \sqrt{7 + 30} = 6.0828$

$$x_2 = \sqrt{7 + 5 \times 6.0828} = 6.1167$$

$$x_3 = \sqrt{7 + 5 \times 6.1167} = 6.1305$$

$$\dots$$

$$x_8 = 6.140$$

$$x_9 = 6.140$$

The sequence of values of x has converged to 6.140 and so the root is 6.140 correct to 3 decimal places.

An alternative rearrangement of the equation

$$x^2 - 5x - 7 = 0$$

is

$$x = \frac{x^2 - 7}{5}$$

If $x_0 = 0.6$ we obtain the sequence 0.6, -1.328, -1.0473, -1.1806, which converges to the root -1.140.

Alternatively, try

$$x = \frac{7}{x} + 5$$

If we start with $x_0 = 6$, then this time the sequence generated is 6.167, 6.135, 6.141, ... which converges to the root 6.140.

The rearrangement $x = \dfrac{x^2 - 7}{5}$

produces a diverging sequence using a starting value of -8.

We get

$$x_1 = 11.4$$

$$x_2 = 24.592$$

$$x_3 = 119.553$$

$$x_4 = 2857.198$$

Many more ingenious rearrangements are possible. For the equation

$$x^2 + 5x - 7 = 0$$

we can add x, say, to both sides to get

$$x^2 + 6x - 7 = x$$

i.e.

$$x(x + 6) = x + 7$$

so that,

$$x = \frac{x + 7}{x + 6}$$

Investigate whether or not this rearrangement will converge to a root of the equation.

Investigation 1

Pupils can be given a number of quadratic equations and asked to devise ingenious rearrangements. They should then investigate whether their arrangements produce converging or diverging sequences for a variety of starting values. Can they find starting values which produce diverging sequences? To assist in the selection of an appropriate starting value (in the sense that it is close to a desired root) pupils should be encouraged to sketch graphs of the relevant functions. On occasions, sequences are produced which neither converge nor diverge but oscillate between two or more values. An example of this behaviour has been given earlier but pupils may stumble across this fact serendipitously.

Investigation 2

Joseph and Reuben are two brothers. They have brought to school a circular pitta bread. At lunchtime Joseph divides it into two parts with a single straight cut so that his piece is twice the area of Reuben's.

The area of a sector of angle $A°$, of a circle, radius r, is

$$\text{Area of sector} = \frac{A}{360}\pi r^2$$

and the area of the triangle shown below is $\frac{1}{2}r^2 \sin A$.

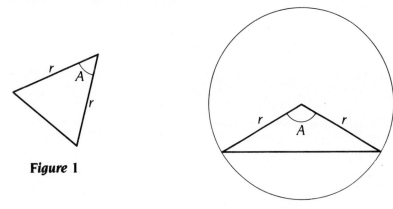

Figure 1

Figure 2

Let pupils try to find the equation which must be solved in order to make the correct cut in the pitta bread.

Referring to Figure 2, we want the area of the small segment to be one-third of the area of the circle.

$$\text{Area of the segment} = \text{Area of the sector} - \text{Area of the triangle}$$

So,
$$\frac{A}{360}\pi r^2 - \frac{1}{2}r^2 \sin A = \frac{1}{3}\pi r^2$$

This equation can be rearranged as

$$A = \frac{180}{\pi}\sin A + 120$$

and starting with, say, $A = 150°$ a sequence converging to 149.3° is generated. Thus, the cut should be made $r\cos 74.65°$ from the centre, i.e. 0.26r from the centre.

Let the pupils devise other rearrangements of this equation and investigate whether they produce converging or diverging sequences. A variety of other similar practical situations give rise to **transcendental** equations such as this one and an iterative approach to their solution is generally the only one available.

Ring roads

With increasing traffic on the roads particularly in major cities traffic engineers have designed and built ring roads or by-passes. The purpose of a ring road is to divert traffic from the city centre and to make it easier and quicker for the traveller who wishes to go from one side of the city to the other.

Suppose the city is roughly circular and of diameter 20 miles. On the open road outside the city boundaries we assume a motorist can travel at a constant (average) speed of, say, 50 mph. On the road that will take him directly through the city centre his average speed will start to decrease as he crosses the city boundary, and continue to decrease until he reaches the centre, where his average speed will be, say, 10 mph. As he progresses from the city centre outwards his average speed will increase from 10 mph to 50 mph until he crosses the city boundary on his outward journey. This is illustrated in Figure 1.

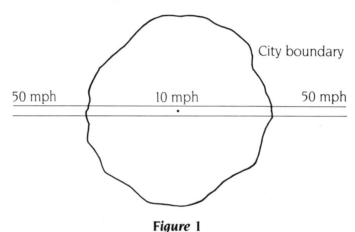

Figure 1

1 Investigate ways of estimating the time taken to cross the city. For example, within the city boundary you might assume various average speeds are achieved in different zones.

2 Now suppose that there is a proposal to build a ring road, somewhere within the city boundary. The traffic engineer has decided that it should be circular and where it crosses radial roads there should be roundabouts. Where it passes through housing estates there will be underpasses so that traffic speed is not unnecessarily reduced. He estimates that on such a road the average speed will be 40 mph.

Investigate ways of finding which is the best position of the ring road based upon your own speed-zone model. That is, how far from the city centre should the road be built so that the journey round the ring road takes less time than the journey through the city centre.

© Tony Croft and Derek Hart,
*Farey Tales, The Lifeguard and Other
Maths Investigations for Higher-Level GCSE*,
Stanley Thornes, 1990

Ring roads: Teaching notes

1 If the increase in speed, v, with distance r, from the centre is linear, the equation of the straight line from $r = 0$ to $r = 10$ is given by

$$v = 4r + 10$$

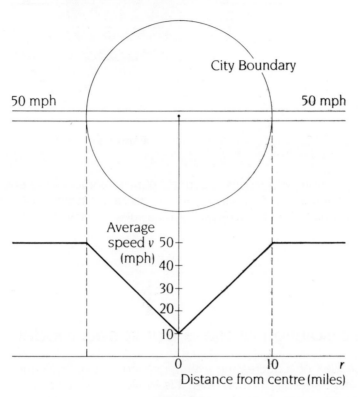

Figure 2

In the first investigation pupils should devise various methods of estimating the time taken to cross the city. An analytical solution of the problem requires calculus so this approach will not be pursued. Before the pupils tackle the full problem a simpler version can be tackled first to familiarise themselves with the methods. Suppose that instead of the speed changing linearly there are a number of zones within the city boundaries where average speeds are maintainable. For example, see Figure 3, on p. 38.

Pupils could calculate the time it takes to cross the city if the speed zones are as shown. They could then devise other 'typical' speed zones and see how this affects the time taken to cross the city.

2 Referring to Figure 3, if a circular ring road were constructed to pass through A, then a car travelling via the ring road moves on a semicircle ABC of radius 5 miles. The length of the road is $5\pi = 15.7$ miles.
At 40 mph this journey takes 23.55 minutes making the total time to cross the city

$$23.55 + 15 \text{ minutes} = 38.55 \text{ minutes.}$$

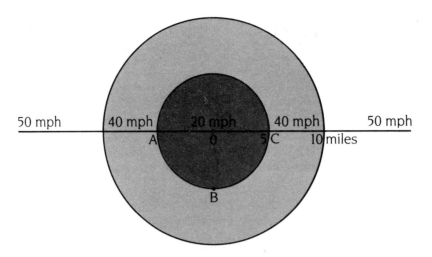

Figure 3

For economical reasons the local council instructed the engineer to design traffic lights instead of roundabouts and zebra crossings instead of underpasses for pedestrians. This reduces the average speed from 40 mph to 30 mph. What happens now?

Suggested solution of the linear speed model

The idea of a decreasing average speed is a difficult one. For example, if a car's average speed is 30 mph when it is 5 miles from the city centre then it will cover, say, $\frac{1}{10}$th mile centred at the point 5 miles from the city centre in 12 seconds (i.e. $\frac{1}{300}$ hour). Similarly, 4 miles from the city centre it would cover $\frac{1}{10}$th mile in 13.8 seconds ($\frac{1}{260}$ hour). This is illustrated in Figure 4.

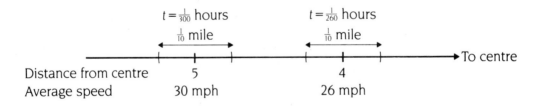

Figure 4

A close approximation to the time for the journey to the city centre can be obtained as follows.

Assume the mean speed between 5 and 4 miles from the centre is

$$\frac{(30+26)}{2} = 28 \text{ mph.}$$

So the approximate time to travel one mile is $\frac{1}{28}$ hours.

38

The following table can be constructed:

Distance from centre (miles)	Average speed (mph)	Mean speed (mph)	Time to travel one mile (hours)
10	50		
		48	0.021
9	46		
		44	0.023
8	42		
		40	0.025
7	38		
		36	0.028
6	34		
		32	0.031
5	30		
		28	0.036
4	26		
		24	0.042
3	22		
		20	0.050
2	18		
		16	0.063
1	14		
		12	0.083
0	10		
		Total	0.402

Thus the time to cross the city is 0.804 hours or 48.24 minutes. (The exact answer, obtained using calculus, is 48.28 minutes.) If the ring road is built 10 miles from the city centre then, at an average speed of 40 mph, the journey will take 47.1 minutes.

11

Going round in circles

1

A single straight line cuts a circle into, at most, 2 regions.

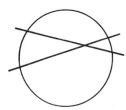

Two straight lines cut a circle into, at most, 4 regions. Under what circumstances would you get only 2 or 3 regions?

(a) Investigate what happens when you use 3 straight lines.

(b) Draw up a table showing the maximum number of regions that can be obtained using 1, 2, 3, 4, ... straight lines.

(c) Try to find a rule which connects the maximum number of regions and the number of lines. Don't simply start guessing but study how new regions are actually formed. For example, how many new regions are formed when you add a third line to two existing ones?

2

If two points are arranged around the circumference of a circle and these are joined with a straight line, we obtain two regions.

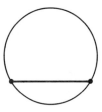

© Tony Croft and Derek Hart,
*Farey Tales, The Lifeguard and Other
Maths Investigations for Higher-Level GCSE,*
Stanley Thornes, 1990

If three points are arranged around the circumference what is the maximum number of regions into which the circle can be divided?

(a) Draw up a table relating the maximum number of regions to the number of points, n, when $n = 1, 2, 3$ and 4.

(b) Can you spot a rule? Try your rule out on $n = 5$. What about when $n = 6$?

(c) Study how new regions are formed when a new point is added on the circumference. Write down a description of how they are formed and then explain the process to your teacher.

WHAT HAVE YOU DONE WiTH REGiON 32 ?

WiTH APOLOGiES TO JAMES THURBER

Going round in circles: Teaching notes

1(a) With three straight lines the maximum number of regions is seven.

(b) If n = no. of lines, and R_n = maximum no. of regions we have

n	R_n
1	2
2	4
3	7
4	11

(c) When a new line (line $n + 1$) is added it should intersect all existing lines (i.e. all n lines). The number of new regions equals the number of existing regions through which the line passes since each region is divided into two. The number of regions a line passes through equals the number of intersections plus one, i.e. $n + 1$.

Therefore, the number of new regions is $n + 1$.

i.e. $$R_{n+1} = R_n + (n + 1)$$

Pupils can verify that this is, indeed, true. This is an example of a first order difference equation, so to obtain an expression for R_n requires knowledge which pupils are most unlikely to have. For completeness we indicate how to proceed: the general solution of this difference equation comprises a complementary function and a particular solution.

Complementary function

This is a solution of $R_{n+1} = R_n$.

The usual technique is to try a solution of the form $R_n = k^n$, giving $k^{n+1} = k^n$, i.e. $k = 1$.

Therefore $R_n = 1^n = 1$.

Particular solution

This is any solution of

$$R_{n+1} = R_n + n + 1$$

and is usually found by making an educated guess based upon terms like $n + 1$.

It is easy to verify that

$$\frac{n^2}{2} + \frac{n}{2}$$

satisfies this equation and is thus a satisfactory particular solution.

The required general solution is then

$$R_n = A + \frac{n^2}{2} + \frac{n}{2},$$

where A is any constant.

Now since $R_1 = 2$, A must equal 1,

i.e. $$R_n = \frac{n^2 + n + 2}{2}$$

2(a) If n = number of points and R_n = maximum number of regions, we have this table:

n	R_n
1	1
2	2
3	4
4	8

(b) Apparently, the rule is $R_{n+1} = 2R_n$
When $n = 5$, $R_n = 16$, so this rule works when $n = 5$.
When $n = 6$, $R_n = 31$, so the rule fails when $n = 6$!
Where is region number 32?

In order to calculate values of R_n algebraic techniques* not normally met until the VIth form are required, but we indicate how to proceed since the arguments involved will be within the ability of some of the brighter pupils.

Suppose that the points $P_1, P_2, \ldots, P_n$ are arranged consecutively around the circle, and that the first $(n-1)$ points have all been joined to each other, but no lines to P_n have been drawn. Now, as we start to include lines from P_n, when each line is drawn, the number of extra regions created is equal to the number of existing regions through which it passes, as each piece is divided into two. The number of regions a line passes through is equal to the number of intersections within the circle it makes with existing lines, plus one. The line drawn from P_n to P_r crosses the lines drawn from each of the $r-1$ points $P_1, P_2, \ldots, P_{r-1}$ to each of the $(n-r-1)$ points $P_{r+1}, \ldots P_{n-1}$ and so it creates $(r-1)(n-r-1)+1$ new regions. We are actually drawing lines from P_n to each of the other $n-1$ points and so the total number of new regions, a_n say, is given by the expression

$$a_n = \sum_{r=1}^{n-1} [(r-1)(n-r-1)+1]$$

$$= \sum_{r=1}^{n-1} -r^2 + n\sum_{r=1}^{n-1} r - \sum_{r=1}^{n-1} (n-2)$$

$$= -\frac{1}{6}(n-1)n(2n-1) + \frac{n^2}{2}(n-1) - (n-1)(n-2)$$

$$= \frac{1}{6}(n-1)(n^2 - 5n + 12)$$

In the derivation of this formula we have assumed that n is at least equal to 2, but since $a_1 = 0$, it is correct for $n = 1$ as well.

$*\sum_{r=1}^{n} r = \frac{n}{2}(n+1),\quad \sum_{r=1}^{n} r^2 = \frac{n}{6}(n+1)(2n+1),\quad \sum_{r=1}^{n} r^3 = \frac{n^2}{4}(n+1)^2$

We can now calculate R_n. Before any lines have been drawn, there is just one region, the whole of the interior of the circle. So

$$R_n = \sum_{r=1}^{n} a_r + 1$$

$$= \sum_{r=1}^{n} \frac{1}{6}(r-1)(r^2 - 5r + 12) + 1$$

$$= \frac{1}{6}\sum_{r=1}^{n} r^3 - \sum_{r=1}^{n} r^2 + \frac{17}{6}\sum_{r=1}^{n} r - \sum_{r=1}^{n} 2 + 1$$

$$= \frac{n^2}{24}(n+1)^2 - \frac{n}{6}(n+1)(2n+1) + \frac{17}{12}n(n+1) - 2n + 1$$

$$= \frac{n}{24}(n-1)(n^2 - 5n + 18) + 1$$

The successive values produced by this formula are

$$1, 2, 4, 8, 16, \textcircled{31}, 57, 99, 163, 256, \ldots$$

There is clearly no 32nd region when $n = 6$, and this example clearly shows the danger of jumping to conclusions!

Wash day

Ariel Automatic detergent can be purchased in powder or liquid forms. The packet sides below give detailed instructions for their use. Investigate ways of finding which is the most economical buy.

Additional information:

(a) A 'cup' is not a well-defined quantity, but is about 4 oz of powder.

(b) The liquid is introduced in a special dispenser which is roughly spherical in shape. Level B represents a volume of 180 ml and level A, 120 ml.

(c) 1 oz = 28.35 g   1 kg = 1000 g   1 litre = 1000 ml.

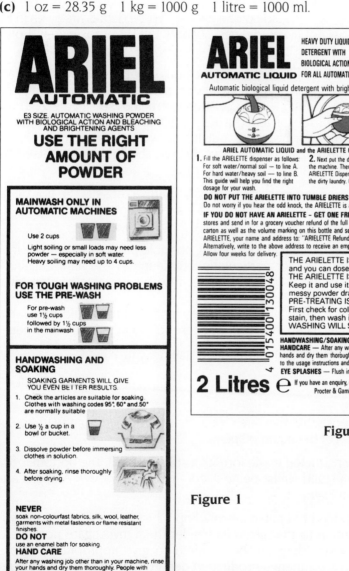

Figure 1

Figure 2

Reproduced by kind permission of Procter & Gamble Ltd

© Tony Croft and Derek Hart,
Farey Tales, The Lifeguard and Other Maths Investigations for Higher-Level GCSE,
Stanley Thornes, 1990

Wash day: Teaching notes

This investigation is in two parts. The first is relatively straightforward, requiring an ability to convert a variety of units. The second is more demanding and is suitable as an extended piece of coursework.

Part 1

A well-known manufacturer of washing powder for automatic washing machines has recently introduced a new product to the market. Traditionally a washing machine requires soap to be introduced, in powder form, to a soap dispenser built into the top or front of the washing machine, the appropriate quantity being determined from the details on the side of the packet. Typical details are given in Figure 1. The 'cup' referred to is not a well-defined quantity but is approximately 4 ounces of powder.

The new product is a liquid. To introduce the liquid soap to the washing machine it is necessary to put a quantity in a special dispenser which is roughly spherical in shape, filling to a pre-marked level, A or B, as instructed (see Figure 2). The level B represents a quantity of 180 ml, and the level A, 120 ml. The dispenser is closed with a perforated lid and is then actually put in the washing machine with the dirty laundry. When the washing machine is switched on the liquid is dispersed 'into the heart of the wash', as the advertisement boasts.

There is some variation in pricing but a local supermarket sells the powder at £1.12 for a 1.05 kg packet, and the liquid at £2.79 for a 2 litre bottle.

Which is the most economical buy? Factors to be taken into account include the different types of wash available e.g. normal, possible pre-washing (some machines allow a so-called pre-wash for particularly dirty laundry) and handwashing. Direct comparison is not at all straightforward because quantities are often given very vaguely –
'handwashing: use half a cup with 10 litres of water' – for the liquid, and
'handwashing: use half a cup in a bowl or bucket of water' – for the powder.

Nevertheless some meaningful comparisons can be carried out.

Part 2

Let the pupils suppose that they are required as part of a design team to come up with the dimensions of the liquid dispenser.

Ideally it is to be constructed in the form of a spherical ball. The bottom is to be flat so that the ball can stand whilst being filled and the two levels A and B are to be marked as shown in Figure 3.

The top is also flattened to enable a screw top lid to be fitted. Using the following information in addition to that given earlier, let them investigate possible dimensions of the dispenser. They will be required to give appropriate dimensions/ measurements to the company's production department so that the dispenser can be produced to hold the necessary volumes of liquid, with the levels A and B marked. There is no need to consider particular design details (e.g. the lid) as these will be dealt with by other staff in the design department. The problem is, however, very difficult to solve and a number of simpler stages can be identified.

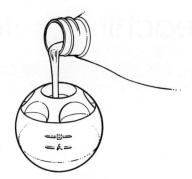

Figure 3

Stage 1

Ask the pupils to come up with a purely spherical design without any levels marked. At this stage don't give them any information other than the formula for the volume of a sphere, and formulae to allow them to carry out any necessary conversion of units (e.g. litres to cubic centimetres).

Important points which they ought to identify include:

(a) the liquid detergent doesn't have to fill the ball – i.e. the ball need not be as small as possible.

(b) What is the smallest possible size of ball?

(c) What is the largest 'sensible' size of ball? It should not take up room meant for dirty washing.

Information

The volume of a sphere of radius r is $\frac{4}{3}\pi r^3$

1 litre = 1000 cc.

Stage 2

Suppose now the flat bottom is to be introduced. Let them investigate the capacities of a variety of designs by asking them to sensibly vary the radius of the ball and the height of the removed cap. They will need to know the volume of a spherical cap:

Information

The volume of a spherical cap is

$$\pi h\left(rh - \frac{h^2}{3} \right)$$

where r, is the radius of the sphere, and h is as shown in Figure 4.

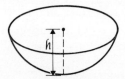

Figure 4

47

Stage 3

Finally, for their chosen design specification, the positions of levels A and B are to be found. In practice this stage is difficult since a direct treatment requires the solution of a cubic equation. However, progress can be made if a trial and error approach is advocated.

The pupils should be encouraged to write up their findings in the form of a report detailing their design specification. A 'life-size' diagram would certainly be useful – let them suggest this. Is their final design practical and sensible? Perhaps a pupil can bring along such a dispenser for comparison.

Extensions

Shapes, other than spherical can be investigated.

Containers to hold other products of different volumes can be designed.

Some possible solutions

Part 1

Take, for example, a normal wash requiring two cups of powder.

1 cup of powder contains 4 oz = 113.4 g

One wash will require 226.8 g = 0.2268 kg.

A 1.05 kg packet of powder will therefore be sufficient for 4.6 washes.

If the liquid dispenser is filled to line A, then a normal wash will require 120 ml. So, from a two litre bottle, containing 2000 ml we would expect 16.7 washes.

Thus, the powder price per wash is about 24p, whilst the liquid price per wash is about 17p.

So, for a normal wash, based on the above calculation, the liquid detergent seems considerably more economical. What would be the annual saving in a typical household if the switch were made from powder to liquid?

Part 2

Stage 1

The radius r of a spherical ball holding exactly 180 ml is found:

$$180 \text{ ml} = 180 \text{ cc}$$

$$\tfrac{4}{3}\pi r^3 = 180$$

$$r^3 = \frac{3 \times 180}{4\pi} = 42.97$$

So, $r = 3.50$

Thus, any sphere of radius greater than 3.50 cm will certainly be large enough.

Stage 2

Referring to Figure 5, the volume of the shaded region is

$$\pi h\left(rh - \frac{h^2}{3}\right)$$

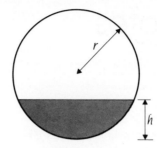

Figure 5

If $r = 4$ cm and $h = 1$ cm, then the shaded region occupies 11.52 cm³.

The volume of the full sphere is 268.08 cm³.

Therefore, the capacity of this dispenser is 256.56 cm³, which is sufficiently large.

For $h = 1$ cm how small can r be?

Stage 3

Let $r = 4$ and $h = 1$, for example.

In order to find the position of level B, referring to Figure 6, we require the volume of the cap given by

$$\pi h_1\left(4h_1 - \frac{h_1{}^2}{3}\right)$$

to be 76.56 cm³.

Clearly $h_1 > h$.

Guess $h_1 = 2$, volume of cap = 41.89 cm³

Guess $h_1 = 3$, volume of cap = 84.82 cm³

So h_1 is a little less than 3, and so on. The exact answer is $h_1 = 2.82$ cm.

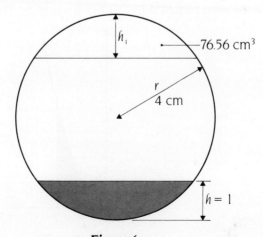

Figure 6

13

Estimating areas

Teaching notes

This investigation is concerned with ways of estimating areas under curves.

Example 1

If the graph is a straight line such as $y = x + 1$ (Figure 1) then no serious problems arise and the shaded area can either be evaluated as the area of a trapezium:

$$\tfrac{1}{2}(4 + 2) \times 2 = 6$$

or as the sum of the areas of the square and triangle:

$$2^2 + \tfrac{1}{2}(2)(2) = 6$$

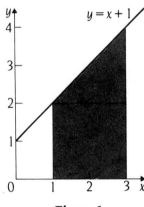

Figure 1

Example 2

If the graph is curved such as $y = x^2$ (Figure 2) then an elementary technique is to estimate the area required by counting squares on graph paper.

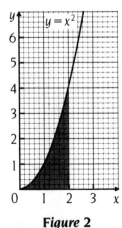

Figure 2

Pupils should now be encouraged to explore alternatives, many of which exist and form the basis of a great deal of more advanced work in applied mathematics.

Suppose we require the area under the curve $y = x^2$ and above the x-axis between $x = 0$ and $x = 2$. The curve can be split into two parts, and a triangle and trapezium drawn as shown in Figure 3. The required area can be approximated by taking the sum of these two areas:

$$\tfrac{1}{2}(1 \times 1) + \tfrac{1}{2}(1 + 4) \times 1$$
$$= \tfrac{1}{2} + 2\tfrac{1}{2} = 3$$

(The exact answer is $\tfrac{8}{3}$)

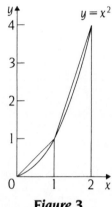

Figure 3

Ask pupils to shade the area they have included but did not want, or wanted but did not include. Let them investigate whether their answers are going to be over- or under-estimates.

For what sort of shapes of curve will this method always over-estimate/under-estimate?

Can they think of ways of improving their estimates? The curve can be divided into four parts instead of two (Figure 4):

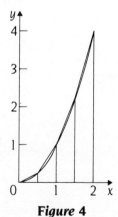

Figure 4

The areas of the triangle and three trapeziums are now

$$\tfrac{1}{2}(\tfrac{1}{2})(\tfrac{1}{4}) + \tfrac{1}{2}(\tfrac{1}{4} + 1)(\tfrac{1}{2}) + \tfrac{1}{2}(1 + \tfrac{9}{4})(\tfrac{1}{2}) + \tfrac{1}{2}(\tfrac{9}{4} + 4)(\tfrac{1}{2}) = \tfrac{1}{16} + \tfrac{5}{16} + \tfrac{13}{16} + \tfrac{25}{16}$$

giving an estimated area of $2\tfrac{3}{4}$.

Ask the pupils to generalise further. This method is the **trapezium rule**.

51

An alternative approach could be to build rectangular blocks to the height of the highest point on the curve within each strip (Figure 5). Clearly taking the sum of the areas of the rectangles will lead to an over-estimate of the area (upper sums). Now try building rectangular blocks on the lowest points of the curve in each strip (Figure 6). The total area of the blocks will now lead to an under-estimate of the required area (lower sums). The mean of the upper and lower sums provides a better estimate. Try increasing the number of strips.

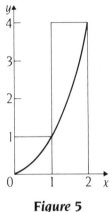

Figure 5

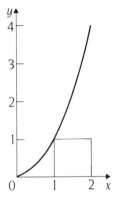

Figure 6

Yet another alternative is to build rectangular blocks at the point of the curve in the middle of each strip. Figure 7 shows that in the case of $y = x^2$ we are both over- and under-estimating in places and there will be a tendency for these effects to cancel out. This method is called the **midpoint rule**.

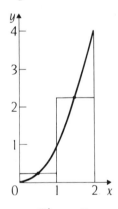

Figure 7

Some problems

Plot the graphs of the following functions and investigate ways of estimating the area bounded by the curve, the x-axis and the given lines:

(a) $y = x^3$ for x between 1 and 2. (Ans: $3\frac{3}{4}$)

(b) $y = \dfrac{1}{x}$ for x between 1 and 3. (Ans: 1.0986)

(c) $y = \sin x$ for x between 0 and 180°. (Ans: 2)

(d) $y = x^3 - 3x + 2$ for x between -2 and 2. (Ans: 8)

52

14

Lifeguards

Most swimming pools have at least one lifeguard. At which point on the edge of the pool would you advise the lifeguard to stand in order to be best placed to assist any swimmer who gets into difficulties.

Pool A

Pool B

Explain carefully what you mean by 'best'.
Substantiate your argument with calculations.

Lifeguards: Teaching notes

Square swimming pool with one lifeguard

We have taken the side of the square to be 4 units (see Figure 1).

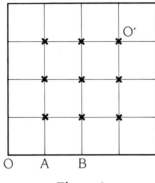

Figure 1

For convenience, assume that the lifeguard can only stand at points, O, A, or B; because of symmetry there is no need to consider any other points.

At least two meanings can be attached to the phrase 'best' position:

(1) a position which will minimise the maximum distance from any point in the pool.

(2) a position which will minimise the 'average' distance from all points in the pool.

(To avoid calculus methods 'all' points in the pool are represented by the nine interior grid points shown in Figure 1. You may wish to include points on the boundary as well.)

Method 1

Clearly the maximum distance from O is OO' and equals $\sqrt{18}$ = 4.24 units. By similar consideration the following table can be completed.

Table 1

Position	Maximum distance
O	4.24
A	3.61
B	3.16

In this case the optimum position is B.

Method 2

Suppose (x, y) are the coordinates of any one of the nine grid points. The distance from (x, y) to O is $\sqrt{x^2 + y^2}$. This quantity can be calculated for all the nine pairs (x, y), where $x \in \{1, 2, 3\}$ and $y \in \{1, 2, 3\}$, and averaged. Pythagoras' theorem is used in a similar way for positions A and B to complete Table 2.

54

Table 2

Position	Average distance
O	2.94
A	2.39
B	2.18

Again, the optimum position is B.

By both of these methods the optimum position is the midpoint of one of the sides.

Rectangular swimming pool with one lifeguard

Most swimming pools are rectangular as in Figure 2.

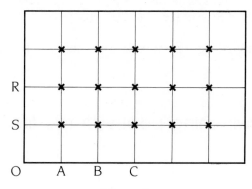

Figure 2

Assume the pool is 6 units long and 4 units wide, and that a single lifeguard can stand at any of the points O, A, B, C, R, S. By symmetry we need not include any more points. The maximum distances are shown in Table 3.

Table 3

Position	Maximum distance
O	5.83
A	5.00
B	4.24
C	3.61
S	5.39
R	5.10

Clearly the lifeguard should stand at the midpoint of the longest side. Did you expect this?

The average distances are shown in Table 4, overleaf.

Table 4

Position	Average distance
O	3.76
A	3.07
B	2.62
C	2.46
S	3.30
R	3.14

Once again the optimum position is the midpoint of the longest side.

Points for discussion

1 Pupils might consider which is the better method of calculating the 'best' position. In the cases of the square and rectangle both methods give the same 'best' point. This is not necessarily true for pools of other shapes.

2 In real swimming pools there is a deep end and a shallow end. Perhaps some kind of weighted average could be proposed.

3 How large need a pool be before there is a need for more than one lifeguard?

Rectangular swimming pool with two lifeguards

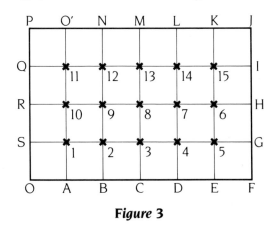

Figure 3

In Figure 3, O, A, B, ..., S are possible points for the lifeguards to stand. We fix lifeguard No. 1 at one of these points and allow the other lifeguard to vary his position from O to S.

One method of finding the best positions for the two men is to find the average distance to the 15 gridpoints from any combination of the two positions. The combination which gives the minimum smallest average distance is the 'best' on this criterion. Clearly, if the two men are standing at C we will have a smallest average of 2.46 (see Table 4). Likewise for the combination (M, M), (M, C) and (C, M).

We are now able to comment upon the point raised for discussion earlier concerning the 'best' method of calculating the optimum position. A method which judges that two people placed at the same point (C, C) gives rise to the optimum position is clearly contrary to common sense. It may be useful for pupils to explore the following:

When the lifeguards are at O and H in Figure 3 their respective distances from point 7, say, are $\sqrt{20}$ and 2 units. So clearly, we can consider point 7 to be 'served' by the lifeguard at H because he is nearer. If we consider all fifteen gridpoints, the least accessible is the one with largest minimum distance. Point 12 has distances of $\sqrt{13}$ and $\sqrt{17}$ respectively from O and H, is clearly 'served' by O, and is the least accessible point. The question is, whether or not we can move the lifeguards so that this least accessible distance is reduced to below $\sqrt{13}$. By trial and error, pupils can choose different positions of the lifeguards and calculate the least accessible point for each position and hence determine the optimum positions of the two lifeguards to serve the swimmers.

For example, if we place the lifeguards at C and M, we find the least accessible point is a distance $\sqrt{8}$ from either lifeguard. Clearly, this is a better choice of position. Is it the best? Note that if both are placed at C, the least accessible point is at a distance $\sqrt{13}$, so this method is more in tune with intuition than the previous one.

More points for discussion

Can the method be modified to take into account the different levels of risk at the shallow end and the deep end, and the possibility of running along the edge of the pool before diving in?

A more advanced problem would be to consider the gain achieved by increasing the number of lifeguards, namely, is the least accessible distance significantly reduced by employing an extra lifeguard?

The problem can be treated at several levels. With a square pool and one lifeguard the distances to grid points need not be calculated but can be measured. The level of sophistication increases as we move from a square to a rectangular pool and from one to two to more lifeguards, and could lead to a general discussion of optimisation problems. In some circumstances pupils could visit and measure the size of their local swimming pool, define a suitable grid, and carry out the previous analysis.

15

Codes and matrices

Teaching notes

This investigation concerns a simply constructed matrix coder and decoder. Suppose you wanted to send a message

DONT TRUST ROBERTS

Stage 1
Divide the message into groups of 4 letters as follows, and then form matrices:

$$\begin{pmatrix} D & O \\ N & T \end{pmatrix}, \begin{pmatrix} T & R \\ U & S \end{pmatrix}, \begin{pmatrix} T & R \\ O & B \end{pmatrix}, \begin{pmatrix} E & R \\ T & S \end{pmatrix}$$

Stage 2
Replace each letter by its position in the alphabet.

$$\begin{pmatrix} 4 & 15 \\ 14 & 20 \end{pmatrix} \begin{pmatrix} 20 & 18 \\ 21 & 19 \end{pmatrix} \begin{pmatrix} 20 & 18 \\ 15 & 2 \end{pmatrix} \begin{pmatrix} 5 & 18 \\ 20 & 19 \end{pmatrix}$$

Stage 3
Choose a 2 × 2 matrix of unit determinant.

e.g. $$\begin{pmatrix} 3 & 1 \\ 5 & 2 \end{pmatrix}$$

This is called a **coding** matrix.

Stage 4
Pre-multiply each of the matrices in Stage 2 by the coding matrix.

e.g. $$\begin{pmatrix} 3 & 1 \\ 5 & 2 \end{pmatrix} \begin{pmatrix} 4 & 15 \\ 14 & 20 \end{pmatrix} = \begin{pmatrix} 26 & 65 \\ 48 & 115 \end{pmatrix}$$

We obtain the matrices:

$$\begin{pmatrix} 26 & 65 \\ 48 & 115 \end{pmatrix} \begin{pmatrix} 81 & 73 \\ 142 & 128 \end{pmatrix} \begin{pmatrix} 75 & 56 \\ 130 & 94 \end{pmatrix} \begin{pmatrix} 35 & 73 \\ 65 & 128 \end{pmatrix}$$

Stage 5
The message is sent as

26, 65, 48, 115, 81, 73, 142, 128, 75, 56, 130, 94, 35, 73, 65, 128

At the other end a fellow conspirator will need to know the coding matrix. This could have been arranged beforehand or could appear in a pre-arranged position in the coded message.

The decoding process is as follows:

Stage 1
Find the inverse of the coding matrix, in this case

$$\begin{pmatrix} 2 & -1 \\ -5 & 3 \end{pmatrix}$$

This is the **decoding** matrix.

Stage 2
Regroup the numbers of the message into fours:

$$\begin{pmatrix} 26 & 65 \\ 48 & 115 \end{pmatrix}, \text{etc.}$$

Stage 3
Pre-multiply by the decoding matrix to obtain the message:

$$\begin{pmatrix} 2 & -1 \\ -5 & 3 \end{pmatrix} \begin{pmatrix} 26 & 65 \\ 48 & 115 \end{pmatrix} = \begin{pmatrix} 4 & 15 \\ 14 & 20 \end{pmatrix} = \begin{pmatrix} D & O \\ N & T \end{pmatrix}, \text{etc.}$$

Investigation

Suggest ways in which a message consisting of 15 letters may be sent. How can messages which contain full stops, commas, punctuation marks, etc., be coded and sent?
Could messages be sent with a 3×3 matrix? What are the difficulties?
Devise other methods of sending messages which are based upon mathematical principles.

This investigation gives ample opportunity to demonstrate a number of important features of matrix algebra.
Why should the coding matrix be chosen to have unit determinant?
What happens if in the decoding stage matrices are post-multiplied by the decoder?
Is matrix multiplication commutative?
Why not use an identity matrix as the coding matrix – it does have unit determinant?

16

The breakfast-time matrix

Construct matrices to hold some of the nutritional information displayed on the cereal packet sides shown below.
Investigate sensible ways in which your matrices can be multiplied by numbers.
Try to find ways in which your matrices can be multiplied by other matrices to give sensible and meaningful results.

A serving of 30 g of *Rice Krispies* cereal provides at least one quarter of the average adult (or one third of a child's) recommended daily amount of vitamins niacin, riboflavin, thiamin, folic acid, vitamins D and B_{12}; and one sixth of the adult (one fifth of a child's) recommended daily amount of iron.

INGREDIENTS
RICE, SUGAR, SALT,
MALT FLAVOURING, NIACIN, IRON,
VITAMIN B_6, RIBOFLAVIN (B_2), THIAMIN (B_1),
FOLIC ACID, VITAMIN D,
VITAMIN B_{12}.

NUTRITION INFORMATION Per 100g	
ENERGY	1650 kJ
	380 kcal
PROTEIN	6.0 g
CARBOHYDRATE	86 g
of which sugars 10 g	
starch 76 g	
FAT	0.9 g
of which saturates 0.3 g	
SODIUM	1.0 g
FIBRE	0.7 g
VITAMINS:	
NIACIN	16 mg
VITAMIN B_6	1.8 mg
RIBOFLAVIN (B_2)	1.5 mg
THIAMIN (B_1)	1.0 mg
FOLIC ACID	250 μg
VITAMIN D	2.8 μg
VITAMIN B_{12}	1.7 μg
IRON	6.7 mg

CORN FLAKES

INGREDIENTS
MAIZE, SUGAR, SALT,
MALT FLAVOURING, NIACIN, IRON,
VITAMIN B_6, RIBOFLAVIN (B_2),
THIAMIN (B_1), FOLIC ACID,
VITAMIN D, VITAMIN B_{12}.

NUTRITION INFORMATION Per 100g	
ENERGY	1650 kJ
	380 kcal
PROTEIN	8.0 g
CARBOHYDRATE	84 g
of which sugars 8 g	
starch 76 g	
FAT	0.6 g
of which saturates 0.2 g	
SODIUM	1.0 g
FIBRE	1.0 g
VITAMINS:	
NIACIN	16 mg
VITAMIN B_6	1.8 mg
RIBOFLAVIN (B_2)	1.5 mg
THIAMIN (B_1)	1.0 mg
FOLIC ACID	250 μg
VITAMIN D	2.8 μg
VITAMIN B_{12}	1.7 μg
IRON	6.7 mg

New recommendations have been made by the Ministry of Agriculture, Fisheries and Food for the way in which nutritive values are displayed. Your favourite cereal has not been changed in any way but the revised methods of calculation may show slightly different values than those provided previously. For more information on our nutrition labelling, please write to CONSUMER SERVICES DEPARTMENT at the address below.

Should this product in any way fall below the high standards you expect from *Kellogg's*, please send the packet and contents to: Consumer Services, UK Office: Kellogg Company of Great Britain Limited, Stretford, Manchester M32 8RA. R.O.I. Office: Kellogg Company of Ireland Limited, Unit 4, Airways Industrial Estate, Clonshaugh, Dublin 17. Please state where and when purchased. We will refund postage. Your statutory rights are not affected.

Reproduced by kind permission of Kellogg Company

© Tony Croft and Derek Hart,
Farey Tales, The Lifeguard and Other Maths Investigations for Higher-Level GCSE,
Stanley Thornes, 1990

The breakfast-time matrix: Teaching notes

Breakfast cereals are widely regarded as providers of vital nutrients and manufacturers exploit this fact in their advertising campaigns. Cereal packets contain a wealth of nutritional information.

Matrices provide a convenient way of storing and manipulating information such as this, and will be the central theme of this investigation.

Amongst the other information given on the **Rice Krispies** and **Corn Flakes** packets is the carbohydrate and fat content per 100 g:

Corn Flakes		**Rice Krispies**	
Carboydrate	84 g	Carbohydrate	86 g
Fat	0.6 g	Fat	0.9 g

This information can be stored in a cereal-nutrient matrix:

	Corn Flakes	**Rice Krispies**
Carbohydrate	$\left(\begin{array}{cc} 84.0 \right.$	$\left. 86.0 \end{array}\right)$
Fat	0.6	0.9

$$\begin{array}{c}\text{Corn Flakes} \quad \text{Rice Krispies}\\ \begin{array}{c}\text{Carbohydrate}\\ \text{Fat}\end{array} \left(\begin{array}{cc} 84.0 & 86.0 \\ 0.6 & 0.9 \end{array}\right)\end{array}$$

This information refers to content per 100 g. However a 'normal' portion would be around 30 g.

The cereal-nutrient matrix for a normal portion is then

$$\frac{30}{100}\left(\begin{array}{cc} 84.0 & 86.0 \\ 0.6 & 0.9 \end{array}\right)$$

i.e.

$$\left(\begin{array}{cc} 25.2 & 25.8 \\ 0.18 & 0.27 \end{array}\right)$$

This is an example of multiplication of a matrix by a number, that is, **scalar multiplication**.

Now suppose that over a period of seven days a portion of cereal is consumed each breakfast time. For example, on four days per week **Corn Flakes** are eaten, whilst **Rice Krispies** are eaten on the remaining three days. We can form a 'portions per week' or 'intake' matrix:

$$\left(\begin{array}{c} 4 \\ 3 \end{array}\right)$$

As in all work with matrices the order is important, the first element referring to the number of portions of **Corn Flakes** eaten, and so on.

Next, multiply the cereal-nutrient matrix (30 g) by the intake matrix:

$$\left(\begin{array}{cc} 25.2 & 25.8 \\ 0.18 & 0.27 \end{array}\right)\left(\begin{array}{c} 4 \\ 3 \end{array}\right) = \left(\begin{array}{c} 25.2 \times 4 + 25.8 \times 3 \\ 0.18 \times 4 + 0.27 \times 3 \end{array}\right)$$

$$= \left(\begin{array}{c} 178.2 \\ 1.53 \end{array}\right)$$

The final matrix represents the total consumption of carbohydrate and fat over a period of one week.

The pupils can now be asked how the average daily amounts can be found from this matrix. This, again, will provide an example of scalar multiplication.

Other points worthy of investigation include:

- Does it make sense to multiply the final matrix by a number like 52 or 4? If so, what does the answer mean?
- Does it make sense to add up the elements of the final matrix? If not, why not?

On the data sheet much more detailed information is given. Pupils should investigate what matrices can sensibly be formed and which can be sensibly multiplied. Note, that not all recommended portions are of the same size and careful treatment is required. In particular, watch any scalar multiplication.

Extensions

A wide variety of food-stuffs now carry detailed information on product content. Look out for suitable packages which can be used to extend this investigation.

Pursuit curves

17

Teaching notes

Whenever a person, object or animal chases or follows another, and moves in such a way that it always faces towards the thing being followed, we say a **pursuit** is occurring and the path of the follower is called a **pursuit curve**. In this series of investigations pupils can plot pursuit curves for a variety of situations and ask when and where, if at all, interception will take place.

Investigation 1

Suppose a car is travelling along a straight stretch of road at a constant speed of 1.5 km per minute. Its location is defined by its distance, s km, from a fixed point O. It is breaking the speed limit for this stretch of road and is spotted by a police car which is in a slip road when it passes point B as shown in Figure 1. The police car immediately gives chase and when it joins the stretch of road at B, it is travelling at a constant speed of 2 km per minute. At this time the first car has reached point C.

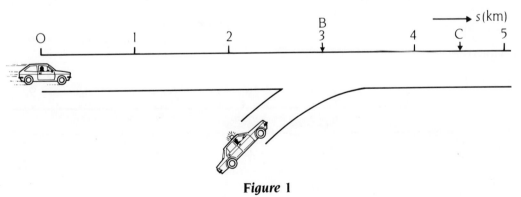

Figure 1

We can plot, on a graph, the positions of both cars at various times to find the time and place at which the police car intercepts the speeding car. Figure 2, overleaf, shows these positions and the point of intersection of the two straight lines gives the time and place of the interception, as $s = 9$ km and $t = 6$ minutes.

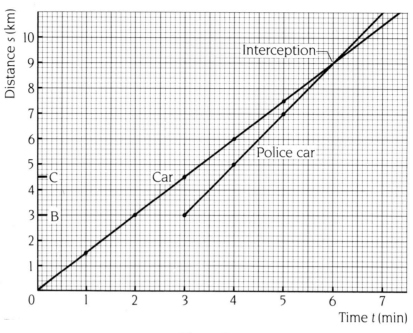

Figure 2

An alternative way of looking at the same problem involves plotting the positions of both vehicles along a single straight line and labelling these positions with the times at which the cars are there. The first stage in this process is shown in Figure 3.

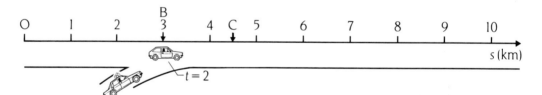

Figure 3

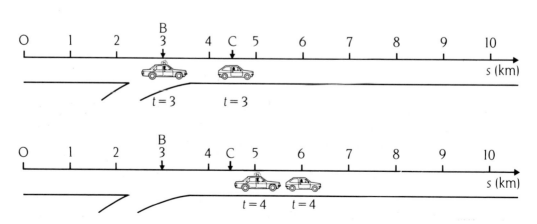

Figure 4

64

Using an appropriate scale, successive positions of both vehicles can be marked (Figure 4) and finally the point of interception obtained.

This method is appropriate to the solution of problems in two dimensions, and enables approximate values of times and places of interception to be obtained, which, if actually calculated would require advanced mathematical techniques.

Investigation 2

Suppose a cat can run along the straight edge of a garden which is bounded by a tall wall, so that there is no escape. The cat can run at 10 m/s. A dog is sitting in the garden, 65 m from the wall, and sees the cat when it is at its nearest point to the dog. The dog immediately gives chase at twice the speed of the cat, and moves in such a way that it always heads towards the cat wherever that might be. Suppose we want to know when, if ever, the cat is caught.

An approximate solution to the problem can be obtained graphically as follows:

Mark the position of the cat, C, when the dog first sees it. The dog D, starts to run towards the cat. We can break down the whole sequence of events into, say, one second time intervals. In the first second the dog moves 20 m as shown and at the same time the cat moves 10 m along the wall.

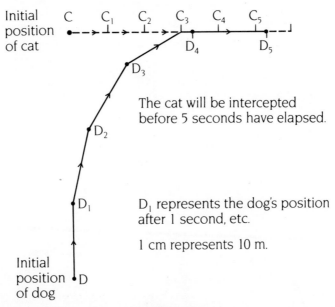

Figure 5

At the end of the first second we can realign the direction of the dog so that it again points towards the cat. Now, using a ruler, we can mark the position of the dog after a further one second as shown. Continuing in this way, the whole sequence of events unfolds and eventually a time and place is reached when interception occurs. The cat will be caught before 5 seconds have elapsed.

A more refined approach would be to break down the event into smaller time intervals, say 0.5 seconds, and an improved solution would be obtained.

The whole path moved by the dog is known as the **pursuit curve**.

65

Investigation 3

The following page shows a Rugby Union Field.

The object of the rugby union game is to score more points than the opponents. Points are scored for goals and for tries. A try is scored if the ball is carried or kicked over the defending team's goal line, and is there set down by a member of the attacking team.

In a game of rugby suppose that one of the players, the **left wing three-quarter**, intercepts the ball on his own 22 m line at A. His aim is to run to the try line and ground the ball at point T before he, himself, is intercepted by the opponents. Suppose here, that only one defender is available, the **full back** at B on the 10 m line. Assuming that the left wing three-quarter can run at 6 m/s and the opposing full back at 8 m/s find where, if at all, the left wing three-quarter will be tackled assuming the full back follows a pursuit curve. (In practice he may well head off the left wing three-quarter, but that would form a separate problem.)

Again, a graphical solution is appropriate. A photocopiable sheet is available for this purpose.

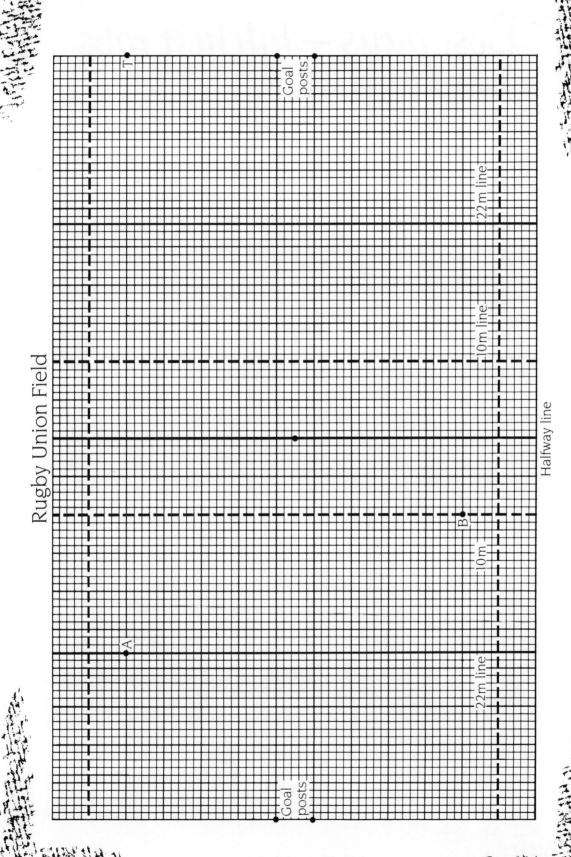

Rugby Union Field

22m line

10m line

Halfway line

10m

22m line

T

Goal posts

A

B

Goal posts

18

Best buys — kitchen rolls

Many supermarkets sell several kinds of kitchen paper — well known makes, and also their own brand. Suppose that there are two brands, Brand A and Brand B. At a casual glance the rolls may appear identical although they are sold at different prices.

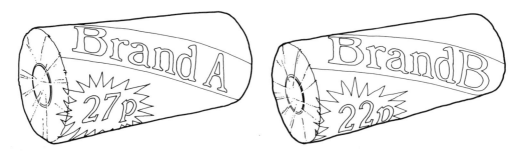

Figure 1

Brand A with internal and external radii 2.5 cm and 5.5 cm sells at 27p and Brand B with internal and external radii 2 cm and 5 cm sells at 22p.

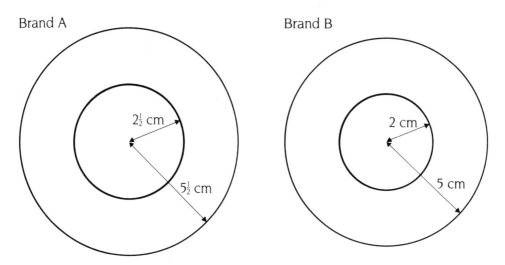

Figure 2

Assuming that the quality of paper is the same in both cases, which is the best buy? Which roll will give the more paper per penny? Investigate a *variety* of ways of obtaining satisfactory solutions to this problem.

From experience we know that the thickness of a single sheet of the roll is about 0.05 cm. Try to estimate the total length of the roll. How many perforated pieces do you think you might get from each of the rolls?

Finally, adjust one or both prices so that there is no difference in value between the two rolls.

© Tony Croft and Derek Hart,
*Farey Tales, The Lifeguard and Other
Maths Investigations for Higher-Level GCSE,*
Stanley Thornes, 1990

Best buys – kitchen rolls: Teaching notes

We suggest that this investigation is set soon after completion of the investigation in Chapter 2, since the results on arithmetic progressions may prove helpful.

The 'amount' of paper can be measured by the cross-sectional area of the roll. This is

$$\pi(\text{outer radius})^2 - \pi(\text{inner radius})^2$$

For Brand A we obtain 24π cm^2 and for Brand B, 21π cm^2.

So the unit price (i.e. price per unit area) for Brand A is

$$\frac{27}{24\pi} = 0.36\text{p}$$

whilst for Brand B we have

$$\frac{22}{21\pi} = 0.33\text{p}$$

making Brand B the better buy.

What quantities are needed in order to calculate the total length of paper?

We need to know the thickness of the paper. Pupils might have investigated this problem separately by, for example, the well-known 'conservation of area' approach. That is, if 20 sheets of paper are placed firmly on top of each other, the total thickness can be measured and hence the thickness of an individual piece can be estimated. The thickness of each sheet has been taken to be 0.05 cm.

We have already stated that the amount of paper can be measured by its cross-sectional area. We know for Brand A that this area is $24\pi = 75.40$ cm^2. If all the roll were unwound, the area of the edge is precisely the same as the cross-sectional area of the annulus. So if L is the length of the strip we get

$$0.05L = 75.40$$

and hence $\quad\quad L = 1508$ cm,

i.e. about 15 m.

Alternatively, consider the following approach.

Although the paper is wound around the cardboard tube in a continuous spiral it is reasonable to assume that it forms a series of concentric circles.

The total length of paper is

    Circumference of 1st circle +
    Circumference of 2nd circle + ... +
    Circumference of outer circle.

i.e. $\quad\quad L = 2\pi(R_1 + R_2 + \ldots + R_N)$

where R_1 is the radius of the first circle, and so on.

The total number of circles is

$$\frac{\text{outer radius} - \text{inner radius}}{0.05}$$

and recalling from Chapter 2 that the sum of an arithmetic series is given by

$$\frac{(\text{first term} + \text{last term}) \times \text{number of terms}}{2},$$

we have for Brand A,

$$L = 2\pi(2.5 + 2.55 + \ldots + 5.45)$$

$$= 2\pi \frac{(2.5 + 5.45)}{2} \times \frac{(5.5 - 2.5)}{0.05}$$

$$= 477\pi \text{ cm}$$

$$= 1499 \text{ cm}$$

Similarly for Brand B we obtain $417\pi = 1310$ cm. Once again, the unit price (now the price per unit-length) can be found and the 'best buy' selected.

Yet another method involves calculating a mean radius and arguing that the total length of paper, considered as concentric circles, is equal to

$$\text{the number of circles} \times 2\pi \times \text{mean radius}.$$

The simplest mean radius is the arithmetic mean of the inner and outer radii. For Brand A

$$L = \frac{(5.5 - 2.5)}{0.05} \times 2\pi \frac{(5.5 + 2.5)}{2}$$

giving $\qquad L = 1508$ cm.

19

Literary fingerprinting

Teaching notes

Much interest is currently being shown in the application of computers to the analysis of the English language. For example, powerful word-processing packages exist which will not only lay out text professionally, but will also check for spelling mistakes or inconsistencies. Even more powerful are a new generation of programs which will check grammar by analysing the structure of a sentence. Other applications include the analysis of pieces of literature to ascertain whether or not different authors use different styles in their writing. It is known, for instance, that Shakespeare wrote 31 534 different words in his works of which 14 376 appear only once. Many academic researchers have used computers alongside statistical packages to carry out detailed statistical studies of facts such as this.

This investigation mimics at an elementary level this sort of work although no computers are necessary. Suppose we take a piece of fiction by a well-known children's author. The author will have a personal style which is reflected in his or her writing and which we can try to quantify in various ways. Over a large number of pages – the more the better – we can count quantities such as:

- the frequency with which words of a given length appear
- the frequency with which sentences of a given length appear
- averages of these quantities.

Even the frequency with which words of a particular type appear (e.g. verbs, adjectives) will help to build up a description of the author and work.

When this data has been gathered it can be displayed graphically in a variety of ways to build up a 'literary fingerprint' of the author and work. If, then, a second and different sort of work is analysed we would expect a different 'fingerprint'.

Pupils can be given the challenge of building up 'fingerprints' in their own ways by selecting books of their choice. Team work here would be especially beneficial and could result in the formation of a 'forensic laboratory' containing a whole range of 'fingerprints' from a wide range of authors and book-types. They should be encouraged to decide upon their own measures and modify these in the light of experience gained. A wide variety of elementary statistical techniques are at their disposal such as mean, median, mode, bar charts, histograms, pictograms, frequency charts, pie charts, scatter diagrams, etc., and should be encouraged.

As an example of what can be done, two books, *Winnie the Pooh* by A. A. Milne, and *The Tao of Pooh* by B. Hoff, have been analysed in this way. They have been written for different audiences – the *Tao of Pooh* being based on the same subject matter but for the adult reader. Two hundred sentences were chosen at random from each book for analysis. The bar chart in Figure 1 shows the word length distributions from which it is evident that Hoff has used slightly more longer words. Perhaps more interesting is the fact that, since both samples represent 200 sentences, Hoff uses many more words per sentence than Milne. A similar analysis of sentence length distribution confirms this.

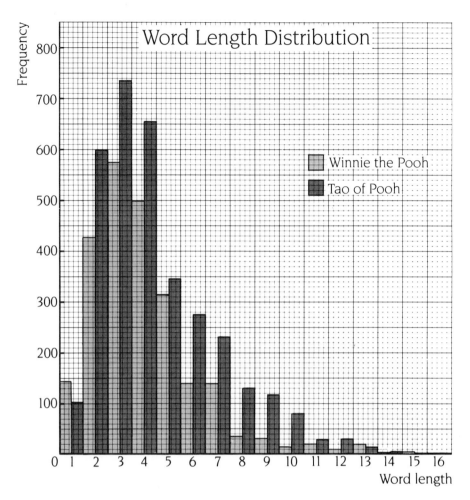

Figure 1

20

Water spouts

Teaching notes

The illustration in Figure 1 is commonly found in elementary physics textbooks and purports to demonstrate that pressure in a vessel of water increases with depth. Whilst this fact is indeed correct the diagram is not, and in this chapter we suggest an investigation which leads pupils to the correct, but not obvious, conclusion.

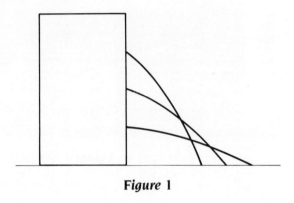

Figure 1

The investigation is based upon three worksheets. The first is written to set up the problem and provoke discussion about the situation, and the second and third provide sufficient information to enable pupils to solve the problem.

Graph 1 is based upon Toricelli's theorem which states that the speed, v, in cm/sec, of water emerging from a small circular hole perpendicular to the surface of a container, a depth d cm below the surface, is given by

$$v = \sqrt{2000d}$$

Graph 2 comes from the standard mechanics formula relating the time of fall, t seconds, of a freely falling object to the vertical distance travelled, h cm,

$$t = \sqrt{\frac{h}{500}}$$

In the absence of any air resistance, the horizontal speed remains constant throughout. The time, t, it takes for the water emerging from the hole to travel its horizontal distance, R (i.e. its range), is the same as the time it takes to reach ground level.

From the graphs, pupils can ascertain the speeds, v, of the different water jets, and the time it takes each jet to reach the ground. Finally the formula $R = vt$ can be used to calculate the range of each jet.

Figure 2, overleaf, shows a photograph of what actually happens.

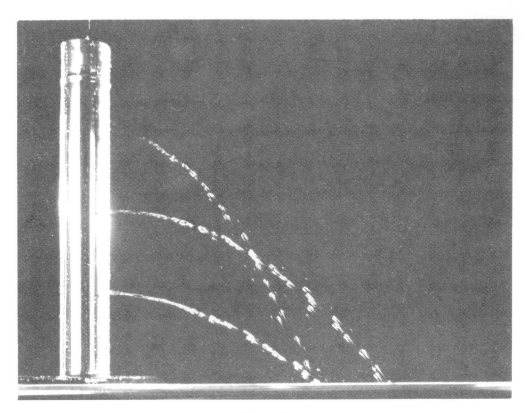

Figure 2

Extensions

This investigation has the potential for use as an extended piece of coursework of an 'applied' nature, and can be used to introduce basic concepts of mathematical modelling.

One extension is to consider what happens if the vessel containing the water is raised above ground level, for example, on to a table. What happens to the paths of the water jets now? Under what conditions can the lowest jet be made to have the greatest horizontal range?

Different behaviour is observed if the holes are replaced with short, narrow, horizontal tubes because Toricelli's theorem is no longer valid.

Suitable source material for project work can be found in articles by J. K. Atkin and A. K. Tamuli in the May 1988 issue of *Physics Education*, vol. 23 and in articles in the Science Notes section of *School Science Review*, vol. 70, March 1989. These articles also give experimental details for those brave enough to want to verify their results!

Water spouts

Worksheet 1

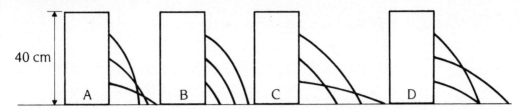

In the diagrams above, each can is kept full of water. The total depth of water is 40 cm. Three holes are placed symmetrically: 10 cm from the bottom and top, and 10 cm apart. The holes are small and circular. Which diagram truly represents the way the water will come out of the holes?

Here are some things to think about before you answer.

(1) The water coming out of the hole near the bottom has a lot of water above it 'pushing' it out.

However,
(2) Just as a tall shot-putter has an advantage over a small one, the water coming out near the top has an advantage over that coming out near the bottom.

If you think none of the diagrams is correct then complete the diagram below to show how you think the water will come out. State your reasons for thinking the water will behave this way.

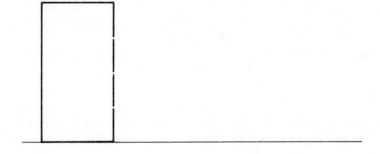

© Tony Croft and Derek Hart,
*Farey Tales, The Lifeguard and Other
Maths Investigations for Higher-Level GCSE,*
Stanley Thornes, 1990

Water spouts

Worksheet 2

To help you further with this investigation here are some facts.

Try to think of the motion of the water as being made up of some horizontal movement and some vertical movement and consider these movements separately.

There is nothing to stop the water continuing to move horizontally at the speed v, with which it emerged and the horizontal distance, R, travelled by the water can be found from the formula

$$R = vt$$

where t is the time for which the motion takes place.

The remaining facts are given in the form of graphs.

Graph 1 The Italian scientist Toricelli, measured the speed at which water emerges from a hole in a can. He found that the speed depends upon the depth of the hole below the surface of the water – the deeper the hole, the higher the speed. The water comes out at right angles to the sides of the can. Graph 1 shows the speed, v, in centimetres per second plotted against the depth, d, of the hole, measured in centimetres. For example, water will emerge at a speed of 200 cm/sec from a hole 20 cm below the surface.

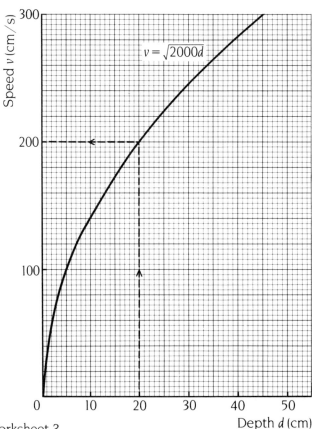

$$v = \sqrt{2000d}$$

Now turn to Worksheet 3.

© Tony Croft and Derek Hart,
Farey Tales, The Lifeguard and Other Maths Investigations for Higher-Level GCSE,
Stanley Thornes, 1990

Water spouts

Worksheet 3

Graph 2 If an object is dropped from a height, h, above the ground then the time, t, it takes to reach the ground depends upon h. Graph 2 shows the relationship between t and h. For example, if we drop an object from a height 50 cm it takes about 0.32 seconds to reach the ground.

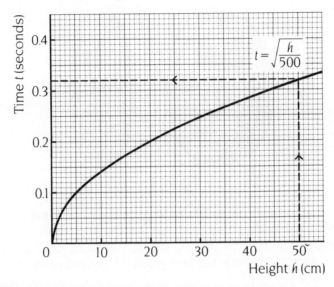

$$t = \sqrt{\frac{h}{500}}$$

Using the information provided on the three worksheets investigate the behaviour of the three water jets.

21

Tyred out

When a car tyre is new it has a tread – a series of indentations cut into the rubber – the purpose of which is to aid road-holding capability and reduce the risk of skidding. Because of this, all cars on the road must have tyres which have a tread of at least the legal minimum depth. When a tyre becomes so worn that the tread is no longer sufficiently deep, it must be replaced.

Figure 1

Because of the tread, the whole surface of the tyre does not come into contact with the road. In this investigation you will have to think of ways of estimating the contact area of a typical tyre. To do this you will need to examine some tyres in order to see how much the contact area is reduced by the presence of the tread.

The problem is this: an eminent scientist from the Environmental Research Committee believes that a major source of contaminant in the atmosphere is all the waste rubber worn from car tyres during their lifetime. He has asked you to estimate the volume of rubber destroyed during the lifetime of a tyre.

(a) Make a list of all the information you will require in order to calculate a reliable estimate.

(b) Suggest ways in which you think you can obtain or estimate this information.

(c) Gather the necessary data and so investigate the volume of rubber used during the lifetime of a typical tyre.

The mass of rubber used is given by the formula

$$\text{Mass} = \text{Density of rubber} \times \text{Volume used}$$

Find out the density of rubber used in car tyres and try to estimate the mass of rubber which disappears.

Finally, conclude your report to the scientist by estimating the mass of all the rubber destroyed in a year from all the car tyres in Great Britain.

© Tony Croft and Derek Hart,
*Farey Tales, The Lifeguard and Other
Maths Investigations for Higher-Level GCSE*,
Stanley Thornes, 1990

Tyred out: Teaching notes

In this investigation there is tremendous scope for pupils to do their own research, the information required being obtainable from tyre depots and libraries, as well as from car tyres! This investigation could therefore be used as an extended piece of work with much of the research to be carried out as 'homework'. Alternatively, or if this is impractical, some of the data below can be given to pupils after they have decided upon what information they need.

Typical data obtained by student teachers in Crewe, June 1989	
No of cars in U.K.	16 000 000
Depth of tread on new tyre	8 mm
Legal minimum tread	1 mm
Maximum width of tyre	156 mm
Minimum width of tyre	130 mm
Average lifetime of tyre	30 000 miles
Radius of tyre	300 mm
Contact area	80% (*See below)
Average mileage of car	10 000 miles per year

*Pupils can estimate the contact area in a variety of ways. Some have made elementary measurements of the various patterns of tread. An interesting attempt consisted of painting part of the surface of a tyre and rolling it across a piece of paper so that more detailed measurements could be made.

The calculation of the volume of rubber lost from one tyre in its lifetime could then proceed as follows:

$$\text{Average width measurement} = 143 \text{ mm}$$

Therefore, the area in contact with the road = 80% of $2\pi(300)(143)$

$$= 216\,000 \text{ mm}^2 \text{ (to 3 s.f.)}$$

With a loss of tread of 7 mm, an estimate of the volume lost is then

$$7 \times 216\,000 \text{ per 30 000 miles}$$

$$= 1\,512\,000 \text{ mm}^3$$

Rubber has a density of about 910 kg/m³, and so with appropriate conversion factors for the units involved, the mass of rubber lost can be estimated. Then, with knowledge of the number of cars on the roads of Britain and their average annual mileage, estimates can be made of the mass of rubber destroyed in the course of a year. Finally, do not forget each car has (usually) 4 tyres!

Extensions

Extension 1

What about the contribution from lorries which have 8, 12 or even more larger wheels?

Extension 2

In wet weather conditions, if surface water is not removed, the tyre does not grip the road, power is lost, and the very dangerous phenomenon of aquaplaning can occur. Then the car actually drives on the water.

A very important role is played by the tread. It serves to disperse the surface water, some of which is forced into the cavities and away from the area of contact.
What sort of quantities of water is it necessary to disperse?

Pupils can estimate this using the data they have already gathered. Suppose, for example, that the car is travelling at 60 mph and there is a 1 mm layer of water on the road. How much water must be dispersed by the tyres each second so that they can grip the road?

Here is one solution.
At 60 mph, the length of road surface covered in one second is about 27 m. If the tyre width is 0.143 m, the area of road surface covered is 3.86 m^2. With 1 mm of surface water, we have a volume of 3.86×10^{-3} m^3 to disperse each second. This is 3.86 litres, or about 0.85 gallons – nearly 7 pints. Pupils will probably be surprised that such a large volume of water is removed each second by each tyre.

This investigation together with the ones in Chapter 6, *Safe driving*, form an interesting extended piece of work applying mathematics to important problems in the real world.

22

Best holiday sites

My uncle George rang me the other day. He has just retired with a huge lump sum and wants to come up to my part of the world to have a little holiday. He has this strange urge to visit some places that he has never been to since he was a little boy. He said:

"I want to stay in one good hotel for the week and drive to and spend a day at the following places:
Snowdon – I want to go up that little mountain railway
Llandudno – to go up the Great Orme on the funicular railway
Chester – to see the Roman remains and the medieval walls
Nantwich – 'cos that's where you live and there's a good pub in the High Street
Stoke-on-Trent – to see the Potteries Museum
Ashby-de-la-Zouch – to see the KP nuts factory and the castle
Liverpool – to see the football grounds."

"All very laudable," I told him, "but you can stay with me."
He wouldn't hear of it.

"It's a hotel for me," he insisted, "I want some comfort and service in my old age."

I asked him what he wanted me to do about it and he pointed out that I was a mathematician and mathematicians were put into the world to solve problems like this.

"There are good hotels in Llandudno, Chester, Nantwich, Stoke-on-Trent, Buxton, and Liverpool," he said, "and I don't mind staying in any of them. You tell me which is the best place to stay."

I asked him what he meant by 'best'.

He was silent for a while and although I couldn't see him at the other end of the telephone I could feel he was giving me one of his quizzical looks. At last he spoke, "It's up to you to tell me what I mean by 'best'. If I knew that there would be no need to ring you up. I would solve the problem myself."

I felt abashed and mumbled that I would try to help him.

The next day I got a good map and was just about to start the problem when . . . to cut a long story short I never actually got around to it. Uncle George wants his holiday next month. He is going to ring me again soon and if I can't help him he will cut me out of his will! I know – why don't you do it for me. Where should Uncle George stay? Where is the 'best' place out of Llandudno, Chester, Nantwich, Stoke-on-Trent, Buxton or Liverpool? When you have done it, tell your teacher so the information can be passed on to me. Many thanks.

Best holiday sites: Teaching notes

Some suggested solutions

1 One meaning of 'best' could be that hotel which made the total distance between it and all the places to visit, as small as possible.

In the table below, the **straight line distances** between each hotel site and each of the visiting places are shown.

| Places to visit | Hotel sites | | | | | |
	Llandudno	Chester	Nantwich	Stoke	Buxton	Liverpool
Snowdon	19	51	66	80	93	52
Llandudno	0	40	57	71	81	35
Chester	40	0	19	32	43	16
Nantwich	57	19	0	14	30	31
Stoke	71	32	14	0	21	43
Ashby	105	67	48	37	39	78
Liverpool	35	16	31	43	46	0
Totals	327	225	235	277	353	255

(The Snowdon mountain railway starts at Llanberis)

The distances to the nearest mile were obtained from a school atlas.

According to the table, the hotel in Chester would be the best.

2 It might be suggested that another meaning of 'best' is that hotel site that has the smallest longest journey. If we look at the longest journey from each site we get:

	Longest journey
Llandudno	105
Chester	67
Nantwich	66
Stoke	80
Buxton	93
Liverpool	78

On this criterion, Nantwich turns out to be the best site.

Extensions

Extension 1

Uncle George is not a fast driver. He has his own personal speed limit for each kind of road. On a motorway, for example, he would not exceed 60 mph and he reckons that this means his average speed on a motorway is 55 mph.

Here are Uncle George's average speeds for some different kinds of road:

	Average speed (mph)
Motorway	55
Trunk Road (dual carriageway)	50
Single carriageway main road	45
B road	40
Urban roads	25

We can express these quantities as a row vector.

$$(55 \quad 50 \quad 45 \quad 40 \quad 25)$$

If we travel at 55 mph average speed on a motorway, for say, 40 miles then it will take

$$40 \times \frac{1}{55} \text{ hours,}$$

so it is not the average speed but its reciprocal that is important. We can construct the vector of reciprocals:

$$(0.018 \quad 0.020 \quad 0.022 \quad 0.025 \quad 0.040)$$

which we shall call **X**.

If we now take a hotel site, say, Nantwich, we can give, as a column vector, the distances on each of the types of road to one of the places Uncle George wants to visit.

Consider the journey from Nantwich to Llandudno.
(Information is readily available from a good quality road atlas such as the AA 3 *Mile Road Atlas*, and distances can be measured using a *Patent 'Map Measurer'* from the Geography Department.)

Motorway	0
Dual carriageway	44
Single carriageway	25
B road	0
Urban roads	3

N.B. This total of 72 miles is clearly greater than the straight line distance given earlier.

The scalar product of the row vector **X** and the distance column vector gives the time taken to travel from Llandudno to Nantwich.

i.e.
$$(0.018 \quad 0.020 \quad 0.022 \quad 0.025 \quad 0.040) \begin{pmatrix} 0 \\ 44 \\ 25 \\ 0 \\ 3 \end{pmatrix} = 1.55 \text{ hours.}$$

This idea can easily be generalised. Suppose we stay in Llandudno then we must visit Snowdon, Chester, Nantwich, Stoke-on-Trent, Ashby-de-la-Zouch and Liverpool.

The distances on each type of road are given in this matrix.

Llandudno to	Snowdon	Chester	Nantwich	Stoke	Ashby	Liverpool
Motorway	0	0	0	0	0	19
Dual carriageway	15	38	44	53	64	24
Single carriageway	4	7	25	25	37	15
B road	8	0	0	0	0	0
Urban roads	0	1	3	5	10	6

This is now premultiplied by the vector **X**:

$$(0.018 \quad 0.020 \quad 0.022 \quad 0.025 \quad 0.040) \begin{matrix} 0 & 0 & 0 & 0 & 0 & 19 \\ 15 & 38 & 44 & 53 & 64 & 24 \\ 4 & 7 & 25 & 25 & 37 & 15 \\ 8 & 0 & 0 & 0 & 0 & 0 \\ 0 & 1 & 3 & 5 & 10 & 6 \end{matrix}$$

$$= (0.59 \quad 0.95 \quad 1.55 \quad 1.81 \quad 2.49 \quad 1.39)$$

Thus the 'total time' to visit all the places of interest from Llandudno is 8.78 hours.

If this is done for all the hotels then the two criteria mentioned earlier can be used:

(a) the 'best' is the hotel with the smallest total time

(b) the 'best' is the hotel with the smallest longest time.

Extension 2

There are at least two additional criteria which your pupils might wish to take into account. The first of these is to award an 'ambience' factor to each hotel site. This factor would measure the pleasantness of the town in which you stayed. These are subjective but here are a few suggestions.

If you like nightclubs and discos then you might give an ambience factor of 0.9 to Liverpool whilst Nantwich might only get 0.3. If you wanted peace and quiet in an ancient town centre you would rate Nantwich and Chester highly but Stoke and Liverpool lowly, ..., and so on. This factor is then multiplied by the distances or times obtained earlier.

The second factor could be a 'journey factor', which again is a number between 0 and 1, and is a measure of the pleasantness of the journey. For example, the journey from Liverpool to Chester under the Mersey Tunnel and down the Wirral skirting Birkenhead and Ellesmere Port is not to be recommended for those seeking the beauty of the English countryside, whereas the journey from Buxton to Ashby, for the most part, passes through some of the finest scenery in England. The former might receive a journey factor of 0.2, whilst the latter could get 0.9.

Don't forget the 'boredom factor' – nearly all the journeys from Llandudno must be along the same road to Chester.

Uncle George, however, is most predictable. He's old (nearly 55!) but has no objections to dingy nightclubs nor discos. He likes nice scenery and loves the seaside!

As a teacher you might want to construct a similar problem for your version of Uncle George but in your part of the world.

Extension 3

There are many possible variants on this sort of problem including, as an example, the optimum location of a set of distribution centres. Take a large supermarket chain which has premises in all the major cities throughout the UK. Suppose you want to establish distribution centres which can be used to store products before they are sent to individual supermarkets. These centres must be within half a day's drive from each major city. How many such centres will be needed and where are they best located? To answer this question an up-to-date road atlas is required showing the major cities and the motorway networks. Naturally, there is no single correct answer, but pupils should be able to come up with a feasible set of locations. They ought to present a case to their 'board of directors' fully justifying their decision to build their required number of centres in their locations.

23

Black-hole numbers

Write down any positive whole number, for example, 45.
Write down all its factors including 1 and the number itself.

$$1, 3, 5, 9, 15, 45$$

Add up all the digits of the factors.

$$1 + 3 + 5 + 9 + 1 + 5 + 4 + 5 = 33$$

This number is called a 'digit sum'.

Now repeat the process with the number you have just calculated and keep on going until you find a good reason to stop. Why have you stopped?

Start again with any other positive whole number. What happens this time?

The number you always end up with is the 'black-hole number'.

Does this behaviour only occur in base 10? Try it in another base.

© Tony Croft and Derek Hart,
*Farey Tales, The Lifeguard and Other
Maths Investigations for Higher-Level GCSE,*
Stanley Thornes, 1990

Black-hole numbers: Teaching notes

The 'black-hole' number is 15. All integers appear to fall into the 'black hole' and no counter-examples have ever been found.

Now, consider other bases.
Take, for example, base 3.
The number 11 has factors 1, 2 and 11 and their digit sum is

$$1 + 2 + 1 + 1 = 12$$

The factors of 12 are 1 and 12 and their digit sum is 11.

Apparently, the numbers 11 and 12 cycle:

$$11 \quad 12$$

Working with the decimal equivalents:

$$11_3 = 4_{10}$$

In base 10, 4 has factors 1, 2 and 4 and their digit sum is 7.
The factors of 7 are 1 and 7 and their digit sum is 8.
The factors of 8 are 1, 2, 4 and 8 and their digit sum is 15. As before, we find that 15 is the **black hole number**.
We see that the behaviour does differ from base to base.

Investigate other bases.

Can pupils find other cycles?

24

Think of a number

Here is a method for producing a sequence of numbers:

(a) Write down any two different digits, for example, 9, 0

(b) Arrange the digits in increasing numerical order to make the smaller of the two possible integers.

09

(c) Arrange the digits to make the larger of the two possibilities.

90

(d) Subtract the smaller from the larger to get a new two-digit number.

$90 - 9 = 81$

Now repeat the above operations on the digits of the new number and then keep on going until there is a good reason to stop.

With the digits 9, 0 we get

$$90 - 09 = 81$$
$$81 - 18 = 63$$
$$63 - 36 = 27 \quad \text{and so on.}$$

Now try these problems:

1 What happens if you continue the above sequence?

2 Repeat the process starting with other two-digit numbers.

3 How many terms of each sequence were calculated before you stopped?

4 Can you predict how long the sequence will be if you start with other two-digit numbers?

5 What is special about numbers such as 81? Can you explain what is happening?

© Tony Croft and Derek Hart,
*Farey Tales, The Lifeguard and Other
Maths Investigations for Higher-Level GCSE,*
Stanley Thornes, 1990

Think of a number: Teaching notes

If a and b are the two integers with $a > b$, then we can write

$$ab = 10(a) + 1(b)$$

and $\qquad ba = 10(b) + 1(a)$

Then $\qquad ab - ba = 10(a - b) + (b - a) = 9(a - b).$

Now, since $a > b$, $a - b$ can only be $1, 2, 3, \ldots, 9$,
so that, $9(a - b)$ can only be 09, 18, 27, 36, 45, 54, 63, 72 or 81.
If the process is carried out with any of these numbers we arrive at another number in the same set. For example,

$$
\begin{array}{r}
54 - \\
45 \\
\hline
09 \\
\hline
\end{array}
$$

Extension

Here is something similar for three-digit numbers.
Arrange the three digits to form the largest number, x. Reverse the order of the digits to obtain y. Find $x - y$. Repeat the process with the digits of this new number. (The three digits must not all be the same!)

e.g. $\qquad 900 - 009 = 891$
$\qquad 981 - 189 = 792$
$\qquad 972 - 279 = 693$

Keep going until there is a good reason to stop!

Here is an outline proof that 495 is special.
Any three-digit decimal number, abc, can be written as

$$100a + 10b + c$$

If we have rearranged the digits to form the largest possible number then $a \geqslant b \geqslant c$. Reversing the digits, we get

$$100c + 10b + a$$

Subtracting, we get

$$100(a - c) + (c - a) = 99(a - c).$$

Now $(a - c)$ can be only 1, 2, 3, 4, 5, 6, 7, 8, 9. (Why?)

So, when we subtract the smaller from the larger the only possible answers are

$$9 \times 99, 8 \times 99, \ldots, 2 \times 99, 1 \times 99$$

which gives us 891, 792, 693, 594, 495, 396, 297, 198 and 099.

If the digits in these three-digit numbers are rearranged to form the largest possible number in each case, then we are left with only five numbers for x:

$$990, 981, 972, 963 \text{ and } 954.$$

89

Reversing the order of the digits to obtain y and calculating $x - y$ yields a new set of numbers:

891, 792, 693, 594 and 495.

If the whole procedure is continued using these five numbers, we eventually conclude that 495 is the unique endpoint of the process.

There are many other unusual and little known properties of numbers or their representations. Although some of the material is advanced in that proof can be difficult, much of it is easy to verify. First of all, let us make the distinction between properties of numbers and properties of their representations. Whether or not a number is prime, for example, is independent of the way in which it is represented (e.g. in roman numerals, binary or decimal systems) – indeed there is scope for investigation here! Some properties are representation dependent. For example, the binary number 1 0 0 0 0 0 1 is a palindromic number. Its decimal representation, 65, is not!

Some of the properties described here were discovered by Kaprekar, the Indian mathematician, who did most of his work some 40 years ago. They all refer to decimal whole numbers.

25

Miscellaneous investigations

Teaching notes

Investigation 1

The Babylonians (2000 BC–600 BC) were an important influence on the development of mathematics, and amongst their achievements was the production of tables of squares, cubes and cube roots.

x	x^3
1	1
2	8
3	27
4	64
5	125

A cubic equation such as $x^3 = 64$ could then be solved by reference to the appropriate table. They also compiled tables for values of $x^2 + x^3$, for example.

x	x^2	x^3	$x^2 + x^3$
1	1	1	2
2	4	8	12
3	9	27	36
4	16	64	80
5	25	125	150

If they wanted to solve an equation such as

$$x^2 + x^3 = 80,$$

they could read off the answer, $x = 4$, from the table.

If they wanted to solve $x^2 + x^3 = 56$ they had to use the table to make an estimate of the solution.

Pupils can:

(a) Investigate various ways of approximately solving equations like this using only the information in the table.

(b) Form new tables for expressions such as $x^4 - x^3$ and then write down and solve equations of their own, finding sensible ways of 'reading between the lines', (see Chapter 1).

Investigation 2

Investigate ways of estimating the surface area of the human body. Make appropriate measurements so that estimates can be obtained for a group of people. Investigate possible relationships between surface area and other anatomical variables such as height and body weight.

Investigation 3

(a) Plot the points represented by the position vectors

$$\begin{pmatrix} -2 \\ 1 \end{pmatrix}, \begin{pmatrix} 1 \\ 2 \end{pmatrix}, \begin{pmatrix} -6 \\ 3 \end{pmatrix}, \begin{pmatrix} 2 \\ 1 \end{pmatrix}, \begin{pmatrix} 6 \\ -3 \end{pmatrix}, \begin{pmatrix} 2 \\ 2 \end{pmatrix}, \begin{pmatrix} 1 \\ -1 \end{pmatrix}, \begin{pmatrix} -2 \\ 2 \end{pmatrix}$$

on a piece of graph paper using a colour or label for each point.
Now consider the effect of multiplying each vector by the matrix M,

where
$$M = \begin{pmatrix} 1 & -2 \\ 1 & 4 \end{pmatrix}$$

Plot the transformed points using the same colour code or labels. As a result of this transformation the points fall naturally into three categories. Let pupils investigate what these three categories are.

(b) Can vectors be found which after multiplication by

$$N = \begin{pmatrix} 2 & -1 \\ -1 & 2 \end{pmatrix}$$

still point along the same line. This means

$$N\begin{pmatrix} x \\ y \end{pmatrix} = k\begin{pmatrix} x \\ y \end{pmatrix}$$

where k is a number.

Hint: Choose some whole number values for k and see if values of x and y can be found which satisfy

$$2x - y = kx$$
$$-x + 2y = ky$$

(c) Investigate the following in the same way:

$$\begin{pmatrix} 2 & 0 \\ 0 & -1 \end{pmatrix}, \begin{pmatrix} -3 & -2 \\ 2 & 2 \end{pmatrix}$$

Teaching notes
(a) The points are transformed as shown in Figure 1.

A: $\begin{pmatrix} -2 \\ 1 \end{pmatrix} \rightarrow \begin{pmatrix} -4 \\ 2 \end{pmatrix}$, B: $\begin{pmatrix} 1 \\ 2 \end{pmatrix} \rightarrow \begin{pmatrix} -3 \\ 9 \end{pmatrix}$, C: $\begin{pmatrix} -6 \\ 3 \end{pmatrix} \rightarrow \begin{pmatrix} -12 \\ 6 \end{pmatrix}$, D: $\begin{pmatrix} 2 \\ 1 \end{pmatrix} \rightarrow \begin{pmatrix} 0 \\ 6 \end{pmatrix}$,

E: $\begin{pmatrix} 6 \\ -3 \end{pmatrix} \rightarrow \begin{pmatrix} 12 \\ -6 \end{pmatrix}$, F: $\begin{pmatrix} 2 \\ 2 \end{pmatrix} \rightarrow \begin{pmatrix} -2 \\ 10 \end{pmatrix}$, G: $\begin{pmatrix} 1 \\ -1 \end{pmatrix} \rightarrow \begin{pmatrix} 3 \\ -3 \end{pmatrix}$, H: $\begin{pmatrix} -2 \\ 2 \end{pmatrix} \rightarrow \begin{pmatrix} -6 \\ 6 \end{pmatrix}$

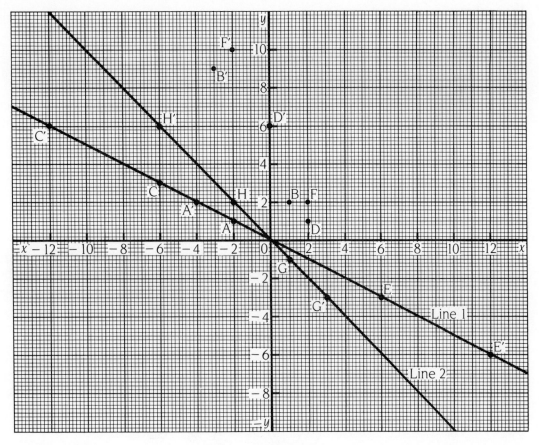

Figure 1

They fall into three categories since some remain on the lines joining them to the origin and others do not. Those that do remain on these lines must lie on only one of two lines. Points on Line 1, namely, A, C and E, are moved away from the origin by a factor of 2 and those on Line 2, G and H, by a factor of 3.

Pupils may alternatively recognise that for some points, the line joining them and their images passes through the origin.

(b) For example, let $k = 1$ so that the equations become

$$x - y = 0$$

and $\qquad\qquad -x + y = 0$

i.e. $\qquad\qquad\qquad x = y.$

Any vectors for which $x = y$ satisfy these equations, so that, for example,

$$\begin{pmatrix} 1 \\ 1 \end{pmatrix} \text{ and } \begin{pmatrix} 3 \\ 3 \end{pmatrix}$$

will point along the same line after transformation. Pupils can easily verify this.

Suppose we let $k = 2$. The equations become

$$-y = 0$$

and $\qquad\qquad -x = 0$

93

so that only the (trivial) vector

$$\begin{pmatrix} 0 \\ 0 \end{pmatrix}$$

which maps to itself, lies along the same line after transformation.

The only other non-trivial case occurs when $k = 3$. Any vector for which $y = -x$ points along the same line after transformation and its distance from the origin is multiplied by a factor of 3.

e.g.
$$\begin{pmatrix} 2 & -1 \\ -1 & 2 \end{pmatrix}\begin{pmatrix} -2 \\ 2 \end{pmatrix} = \begin{pmatrix} -6 \\ 6 \end{pmatrix} = 3\begin{pmatrix} -2 \\ 2 \end{pmatrix}$$

Investigation 4

A shoe manufacturer is interested in different ways of threading a shoe lace through the holes in the shoes shown below. Both ends of the lace should emerge at the top end of the shoe. Investigate various ways in which the lace can be threaded so that he can reduce the amount of lace needed and so save his company money.

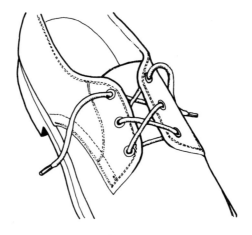

Figure 2

Investigation 5

In a small examination room desks are arranged in the form of a square with the invigilator sitting at the front.

e.g.

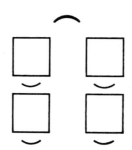

The examination rules say that candidates sitting the same examination paper may not sit alongside each other but any other arrangement is permissible.

For example, if A and B are two different papers, then

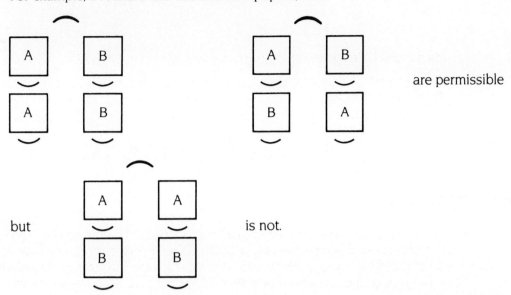

are permissible

but   is not.

If all examination rooms are 'square' find the maximum number of candidates for any one examination paper, if the room holds 3 × 3 tables, 4 × 4 tables, etc, and two examinations are to take place. Generalise the result.

Can you find a formula relating the maximum number of candidates to the size of room?

Suppose three examinations are to take place in the room. What are the various possible combinations of numbers of candidates allowed to sit each paper?

Assessment Checklist

Criteria for awarding marks for internally assessed GCSE Investigations

Assessment of investigational work is significantly more subjective than traditional forms of assessment, and Examination Boards have produced their own criteria and marking schemes. The following points can be used as **general guidelines** in the formulation of a marking scheme for a particular investigation. Clearly, not all the points indicated will be relevant to all investigations, and some of the more demanding qualities described may be beyond the ability of the less able.

Understanding	Very well	Amply	Superficially	No evidence
1 Is the pupil able to produce a clear statement of the problem				
(a) verbally?	☐	☐	☐	☐
(b) in written form, identifying its key features?	☐	☐	☐	☐
2 Is there evidence of a clear understanding?	☐	☐	☐	☐
Planning				
3 Is the pupil able to formulate appropriate questions to be asked?	☐	☐	☐	☐
4 Can the pupil indicate where any necessary information or data can be obtained?	☐	☐	☐	☐
5 Is there evidence of a strategy developing?	☐	☐	☐	☐
6 Can the pupil recognise how a situation can be interpreted mathematically?	☐	☐	☐	☐
7 Can an appropriate method for tackling the problem be identified?	☐	☐	☐	☐
Carrying out the investigation				
8 Can the pupil gather necessary information either from worksheets/data sheets, books or from other sources available, for example, in the library?	☐	☐	☐	☐
9 Does the pupil understand the data that has been given or found?	☐	☐	☐	☐
10 Can the pupil extract from an amount of information or data, its relevant parts?	☐	☐	☐	☐

	Very well	Amply	Superficially	No evidence

11 Can the pupil make relevant calculations, demonstrate mathematical knowledge and answer technical questions? ☐ ☐ ☐ ☐

12 Is the pupil able to draw conclusions, identify patterns, etc? ☐ ☐ ☐ ☐

13 Can areas of further investigation be identified? ☐ ☐ ☐ ☐

14 Can the pupil suggest modifications to the problem and invent new problems? ☐ ☐ ☐ ☐

15 Is there the suggestion of comparison of a variety of techniques for tackling a problem? ☐ ☐ ☐ ☐

16 Can the pupil work in a logical and organised way

   (a) individually? ☐ ☐ ☐ ☐

   (b) co-operatively? ☐ ☐ ☐ ☐

17 Is the pupil aware of any assumptions which have been made? ☐ ☐ ☐ ☐

Summarising and communicating

18 Can the pupil write up a clear report of his/her investigation, identifying any findings and making wide and effective use of mathematical language? ☐ ☐ ☐ ☐

19 Can the pupil identify what has been learnt? ☐ ☐ ☐ ☐

20 Is the pupil aware of the dependence of conclusions on assumptions already made? ☐ ☐ ☐ ☐

21 Can any findings be communicated orally to

   (a) the teacher? ☐ ☐ ☐ ☐

   (b) other pupils? ☐ ☐ ☐ ☐

22 Can the pupil identify any shortcomings? Is the validity of any models used questioned? ☐ ☐ ☐ ☐